THE
PUNISHMENT
CURE

THE PUNISHMENT CURE

How aversion therapy is being used
to eliminate SMOKING, DRINKING,
OBESITY, HOMOSEXUALITY ...
and practically anything else

Stephen J. Sansweet

MASON/CHARTER

NEW YORK 1975

Library of Congress Cataloging in Publication Data

Sansweet, Stephen J   1945–
  The punishment cure.

  Bibliography: p.
  1. Aversion therapy.   I. Title.
RC489.B3S18   616.8'5   75-30940
  ISBN 0-88405-118-8

For mother and dad, who always believed
And for Barbara, for sharing

PUNISHMENT IS A SORT OF MEDICINE.

—Aristotle
NICOMACHEAN ETHICS

CONTENTS

PREFACE

The widespread use of a psychological technique involving punishment is bound to be controversial. The fact that aversion therapy is little understood yet often overpraised, that research in the field is usually communicated in jargon that only remotely resembles English, and that the treatment is used despite the lack of standardized procedures, fuels the controversy. This book is an attempt to explain aversion therapy, to trace its origins and applications, and to set forth all sides of the central issue: Should the punishment cure be used; if so, by whom, in what situations, and under what guidelines? Although the book draws some definite conclusions and suggests others, it is clearly up to the reader to make a final judgment.

Punishment as a weapon of retaliation has been around as long as mankind, but it has been a relatively short time since men of science have dignified it as a social and medical tool. The word still conjures up negative associations and a question arises about what to cover in a book dealing with punishment as therapy. The field clearly includes injecting an inmate with a drug that makes his body go limp and stops his breathing for several minutes. But is it aversive to awaken a young bed wetter from a deep sleep with a bell when he starts to urinate? I think so, and therefore whenever a doubt has arisen I have tended toward including a subject rather than excluding it. The book does not attempt to delve into the large and fascinating body of work in which aversion therapy has been used on animals. Rather, its focus is the present-day use of aversion therapy and related techniques on humans in clinical settings for everything from nail biting to homosexuality.

This book had its beginnings in a front page story in the *Wall Street Journal* and all together entailed more than a year of research. I would like to thank the scores of men and women mentioned in the book, many of whom gave of their time for interviews or sent along copies of their latest research. I am indebted to the publishers of the numerous scientific journals cited in the bibliography for the use of many case studies that hopefully enliven the text. Ron Cooper, a friend and colleague, gets a special nod for his thankless task of helping to whip the manuscript into shape with a heavy editing pencil. Thanks also to Inga Holmner, assisted by Judy Gale, for typing the manuscript. Louise Scott, a young and charming British art student, more than met my expectations with her creative sketches. Finally, a hearty thanks to my friends and relatives who put up with me and helped perk up my spirits during some difficult days. The author, as they always say, is of course solely responsible for any errors in fact or judgment.

Stephen J. Sansweet
Marina del Rey, California

Chapter I

THE REWARDS OF PUNISHMENT

In a Los Angeles hospital, a middle-aged alcoholic businessman lifts a scotch and soda to his lips and immediately becomes nauseous, thanks to a drug injection he received several minutes before.

In a Connecticut prison, a convicted child molester watching a slide show grimaces when a picture of a pretty eight-year-old girl flashes on the screen and he gets a jolt of electricity to his right thigh.

In a London clinic, an overweight young secretary given verbal suggestion pictures herself in a room filled with her favorite fattening goodies. Then, on cue, she "sees" that the cakes and pies are teeming with worms and maggots.

These three souls have not fallen into the clutches of a worldwide gang of do-badders. They are not going through some sort of sadistic ritual or torture. All are suffering from problems—chronic drinking, child molesting, overeating—which they have not been able to overcome and which have made their lives miserable. So they, and thousands like them all over the world, are undergoing the most controversial, yet surprisingly little-known, treatment being used to alter human behavior. Psychologists call it aversion therapy. In reality, it is the stick part of the old "carrot and stick" routine. It is, in fact, the punishment cure.

1

At its simplest, aversion therapy involves linking some kind of unpleasantness with an unwanted behavior in an attempt to eliminate or modify that behavior. A mother who spanks her five-year-old son after he breaks the cookie jar is applying her own form of "aversion therapy" to make sure he won't break the next one. How many parents have realized that they were pseudopsychologists when they painted Junior's fingers with a foul-tasting liquid to stop the tyke from sucking his thumbs? Although aversion therapy as such may be part of the new psychology of behavior modification, aversive techniques to control behavior are as close as common sense and as old as mankind. The difference is that these techniques now have been given some order, some scientific rationale, and placed in the hands of doctors and psychologists who have advanced far beyond cookie jar breakers and thumbsuckers. Today they deal with autistic children, smokers, homosexuals, people who are afraid to fly, even fingernail biters. The list is limited only to the extent that people stop coming up with new maladies, an unlikely event indeed.

Critics of the punishment cure range from psychologists themselves who either think it does not work or have qualms about using it, to civil libertarians who see it as George Orwell's *1984* and Anthony Burgess' *A Clockwork Orange* rolled into one scary little ball. They have nightmares of living things being turned into lifeless machines—clockwork oranges—much like Burgess' anti-hero, Alex. In the book the sadistic English bully is imprisoned for a long list of violent crimes. In return for a promise of immediate release, Alex submits to a fictionalized form of aversion therapy that makes him retch at the very thought of violence. The boy becomes helpless upon release, falls prey to the violent world around him, and almost commits suicide before the treatment wears off. The critics' worst fears seemed to be confirmed when a program stunningly reminiscent of *A Clockwork Orange* was carried out at two California prisons. Other projects, not nearly as harsh, are still underway in state prisons across the United States. It is one thing, however, to note that aversion therapy has a large potential for abuse and quite another to say that it therefore should be banned altogether. That same logic could apply to every technological advance man has made in this century, from the automobile to atomic energy.

To its most enthusiastic backers, people like Atlanta psychologist Barry A. Tanner, aversion therapy is a "humanizing" procedure and is not as unpleasant as, say, dental work. Tanner gets a little emotional about the criticism. "Dentists are not considered dehumanized when they violently remove dental decay or an entire tooth," he says. "A surgeon is not considered immoral when he destroys tissue in order to correct or avoid still greater harm; and a dynamic therapist is not considered brutal when he subjects his clients to painful emotional behavior in the hope that he may ultimately achieve emotional relief through insight." The electric shocks, nausea drugs, or imaginary horrors used by aversion therapists are delivered only "in order to replace behavior which is defined both by society and the subject as undesirable with behavior that both consider to be more desirable," says Tanner, who reports great success in changing homosexual behavior.

•

There is no master registry that lists how many psychologists and others use aversion therapy, and the method often passes under another name or as part of an overall behavioral treatment program. Recently there has been increased public awareness, although not necessarily understanding, of the technique (which is not so strange since few psychologists can agree on what it is all about). By mid-1974 aversion ther-

Reprinted by permission of the Chicago Tribune. Copyright 1974. All rights reserved.

apy had become enough a part of the pop culture for cartoon-
ist Pete Hansen to satirize it in his "Lolly" newspaper comic
strip and for "Dear Abby" to recommend it in her widely read
advice column for exhibitionists who want help in covering
up. Another indication: At the 1962 annual meeting of the
American Psychiatric Association, few of those in attendance
had even heard of aversion or its relatives. At the 1969 meeting more than 600 psychiatrists attended a day-long program
called "Refresher Course in Behavior Therapy."

In the past decade, and mainly in the last five years or so,
hundreds of case studies and experiments with aversive techniques have been written up in a score of medical and psychological journals. Even while research continues and
debate rages as to how, or even if, aversion therapy works, its
practitioners have taken it from the experimental lab into the
treatment clinic. The work is being carried out mainly in the
United States, Great Britain, Canada, and Australia, but it is
also popular in Western Europe, the Soviet Union, and other
Communist bloc countries. The psychology departments at
several big colleges and universities in the United States have
become oriented toward behavior therapy as a whole. Work
on aversion techniques there and at such publicly funded
institutions as Veterans Administration and county hospitals
has been spurred by grants from the National Institute of
Mental Health and other governmental agencies. In the last
few years dozens of private, profit-making behavior modification clinics have sprung up across the country. Some depend
almost entirely on aversion therapy to stamp out one particular kind of problem, such as smoking. Others combine aversion with additional behavioral techniques to treat a broad
range of complaints. These clinics do not have to be licensed,
rarely report their failures or even claims of success, and are a
big unknown in the equation.

Aversion therapy has kept pace with the tremendous
growth of the entire field of behavior therapy, which is busily
challenging the basic concepts of psychiatry. Traditional psychotherapy, or the "talking cure" as an early patient called it,
stems from the work of Sigmund Freud. It too seeks to modify
behavior, but through verbal interaction instead of direct intervention. Critics charge that it takes too long, costs too

much, can be used on only a limited variety of problems, and just does not have a good record of success.

Behavior therapy, with its more specific and limited objectives, is said to take less time and money and therefore is beneficial to a greater number of people. Instead of theoretical concepts, behavior therapy is based mainly on learning principles developed through experiments with animals. (That leads one researcher to caution, "Monkeys are *not* furry little men with tails!") The goal of behavior therapists is to alter directly a person's observable behavior rather than his thoughts and feelings; the latter will often follow the former, they believe. The granddaddy of behavior therapy was Ivan Pavlov, the Russian physiologist. He is famous for his experiments in conditioning, in which behavior is modified so that an action or response previously associated with one stimulus becomes associated with another. Pavlov saw that when he presented his dogs with food (a natural or *unconditioned stimulus*) they would salivate (a natural or *unconditioned response*). After ringing a bell a number of times (an unnatural or *conditioned stimulus*) before presenting the food, Pavlov saw that the dogs would then salivate to the sound of the bell alone (a *conditioned response* or reflex). The new response would eventually extinguish if there was no reward of additional food, Pavlov noted. (Obviously, Pavlov is also responsible for uncorking the flood of jargon and contradictory theories that now muddy the waters.)

An American psychologist, John B. Watson, adapted Pavlovian techniques for humans and founded the behaviorist school of psychology in the 1920s. Watson will long be remembered for his conditioning of Little Albert, a carefree 11-month-old infant. Albert was shown a white rat with which he had previously enjoyed playing. This time, however, one of Watson's associates stood behind Albert and forcefully struck a steel bar, making a loud noise that upset the child. Within a short time after repeatedly pairing the loud noise with the sight of the rat, Albert became fearful and started crying when the rat alone was presented. His fear spread to a rabbit, a dog, and even a sealskin coat. (If the conditioning of Little Albert seems quite similar to Pavlov's dogs, that is because aversive techniques retain the closest

kinship to animal lab experiments of any of the behavior modification methods.) Watson's theories on human behavior
were too mechanistic. He explained everything in physical
and chemical terms and would not acknowledge that there
was anything of import beyond overt and observable
behavior.

Going beyond Pavlovian, or *classical conditioning*, another group of psychologists, including the controversial B.F.
Skinner, came up with *operant conditioning* or reinforcement
theory. Different consequences—both positive and negative—
determine what behavior will be learned, they say. To increase the rate a rat presses a bar, researchers give it food
pellets immediately after each press; to eliminate the behavior, the rat is jolted with electric shocks. The mother who
punishes her child for breaking the cookie jar might also *reward* him with a piece of candy after he engages in some
behavior she is trying to foster, such as tying his own shoe-
laces or flushing the toilet. Skinner insists that every action is
determined by the environment and that all behavior is
"shaped and maintained by its consequences." But he believes only in the reward half of the theory. "A person who
has been punished is not less inclined to behave in a given
way; at best, he learns how to avoid punishment," Skinner
writes in *Beyond Freedom and Dignity*, his own plan for a
highly controlled "brave new world."

•

Physicians, and wardens, throughout history have had a
very positive attitude toward changing behavior with aversive
techniques. Leaving the more obvious methods of torture
aside, many of the ancient ways have survived until today in
only slightly altered form. Now, of course, they have the
weight of scientific theory behind them. When used on people
diagnosed as "insane," aversive methods, or treatment by
"shock and commotion," were supposed to cause a sufficiently severe assault on the body to alter a patient's mind. Doctors
had recognized that a natural shock or illness sometimes
caused the insane to become rational again. Favorite early

techniques included nearly drowning the patient or dripping tons of cold water on his head. Another choice method was swinging or spinning a patient about in a revolving chair 100 times a minute until he convulsed or blacked out.

One of the most "modern" aversive techniques, electricity, is really one of the oldest. The ancient Greeks used the electric torpedo or crampfish applied live to parts of the body. It was great for nagging headaches. In the eighteenth century, frictional electric machines were invented and popularized by, among others, John Wesley, the founder of Methodism. He used it "in nervous cases of every kind." In a book published in 1760 Wesley wrote: "How much Sickness and Pain may be prevented or removed, and how many Lives saved by this unparallel'd Remedy. And yet with what Vehemence has it been opposed?" John Birch , a British surgeon in the latter part of the same century, reported curing a singer of his excessive "depression of spirits" by passing six electric shocks through his head daily for several weeks.

Chemicals to induce nausea and vomiting also have been popular for centuries. The eleventh century Arabian physician, Avicenna, prescribed camphor oil which, by the seventeenth century, was being used for all types of nervous maladies. Taken internally the oil produced sweating, vomiting, and diarrhea; in large doses it could cause convulsions (and was resurrected in the early 1930s to use on schizophrenics for that purpose). Sir Alexander Morrison, a British physician credited with instituting the first formal lectures on psychiatry in 1823, used camphor to treat "monomania with unnatural propensities." Today that is called "homosexuality." Since the "crime against nature" was then punishable by death (burning or burying alive were favored), Sir Alexander wrote in 1838 that "it is a consolation to know that it [homosexuality] is sometimes the consequence of insanity." He reported that of nine cases treated with large doses of camphor, two were "cured."

The most interesting early account of aversive treatment —astonishing for its resemblance to present-day methods— was written by Dr. Benjamin Rush, a signer of the Declaration of Independence and the father of American psychiatry. In a pamphlet written toward the end of the eighteenth century, *An Inquiry into the Effect of Ardent Spirits upon the Human Body and Mind*, Dr. Rush said his treatment made use of "that operation of the human mind which obliges it to associate ideas, accidentally or otherwise combined, for the cure of vice. . . . By means of other impressions . . . [I can] destroy . . . the influence of all those circumstances with which the recollection and desire of spirits are combined." In an experiment, Dr. Rush "tempted a Negro man, who was habitually fond of ardent spirits, to drink some rum" which had been doctored with a few grains of tartar, a nauseant still used today. This "sickened and puked him to such a degree that . . . he could not bear the sight, nor the smell of spirits for two years afterwards."

Western society was not alone in developing the punishment cure. The Ashanti tribe, in what is now Ghana, used a subtle technique on young boys who still wet their beds at night after they got to be about three and a half years old. Sociologist R. S. Rattray published this fascinating account in 1929: "Should the child at first wet the sleeping-mat during the night, the father will not flog him, but will call in small boys and girls about his son's own age and tell them to come and catch this boy and make him dance a dance called *nonsua bono*. He will be tied up in his bed-mat, taken to 'the bush' and dressed in *nsansono* [a prickly, stinging plant]; water will be thrown over him and the boys will sing: 'You wash your sleeping-mat in the night; you wash your cloth in the night.' . . . Sometimes a child who has a strong *sunsum* (spirit) will die after such ridicule." Today, when a similar technique is used with transvestites, it is called "shame aversion therapy."

The first aversion experiments in this century, based on modern learning and conditioning theories, were apparently carried out on Russian alcoholics in the late 1920s. In the next two decades American psychologists entered the fray with aversive conditioning of homosexuals, bed wetters, and alcoholics, all of which is detailed in later chapters. It was not until the 1950s that behavior therapy as a whole really caught on, and it took another decade for aversion therapy to make large inroads in the clinics. Finally, therapists became encouraged by the ground swell of published studies reporting success in case after case of seemingly intractable behavioral problems.

•

People who practice and write about their work with aversion therapy agree on very little. Like quoting the Bible, it is possible to find substantiation for any side of an argument by carefully picking your source. There is some agreement, though, that aversive procedures generally fall into three main categories: punishment, escape, and avoidance. In the *punishment* procedure, a response (such as starting to drink a highball) produces a noxious stimulus (like a brief electric shock). In *escape*, the electric shock is present, but putting down the glass terminates it. In the *avoidance* procedure, there is no shock and the patient knows it will remain absent as long as he engages in some other nondrinking behavior, such as a social conversation with the therapist.

Some psychologists add variations to the basics. Among these: a *preservation* procedure in which the electric shock is present and drinking behavior prolongs its presence; an *anxiety* situation in which the alcoholic patient cannot do anything to avoid or escape from a prolonged shock; and a *relief* procedure in which the stimulus following the shock (such as social conversation in a tavern setting) takes on positive and reinforcing aspects of its own. Another method is called *time-out from reinforcement*. The patient might be positively rewarded for acceptable behavior with tokens exchangable for cigarettes or a visit from his wife; unacceptable behavior would result in a withdrawal of some tokens. Regardless of the jargon and the number of categories, these techniques are all punishment in the commonly accepted sense.

Many traditional psychotherapists are opposed to behavior therapy, and aversion therapy in particular, because they say it treats just the symptoms and does not seek to mount a search and destroy mission for the underlying causes of the problem behavior. Some express fear that elimination of one symptom will lead inexorably to its substitution by another, although this has been disproved to the satisfaction of most therapists. Other critics say aversion is unethical, immoral, dehumanizing, and downright nasty for both the patient and therapist. "Life is too full of punishment to make it necessary or advisable to administer more of it in the clinic," says psychologist J. G. Sheehan. "Therapists who use punishment are probably incompetent to use anything else, or have a neurotic need to assume the role of the punisher as a reassurance against their own fear of being in the role of the one punished," he adds with a Freudian flourish.

Much of the criticism is answered in a thoughtful and well-written college-level text, *Principles of Behavior Modification*, by Albert Bandura, a professor at Stanford University and a former president of the American Psychological Association. Bandura says that the so-called psychic pathology, complexes, or syndromes that most psychiatrists assume underlie all behavioral malfunctioning are merely abstractions they have made from the observable behavior itself. (A man does not get along with his boss and feels like killing him; ergo, he has an Oedipus complex.) Behavior that is harmful to an individual, or is widely at variance with societal standards, is not symptomatic of some sort of mental disease, Bandura argues. It is simply a way that person has learned to cope with environmental and self-imposed demands. That does not mean that all behavior is programmed by external variables out of our control. Behavior is also controlled by internal, symbolic inputs—our thoughts, perception, and emotions. The real questions to be concerned with in behavior modification, Bandura says, are whether a given set of conditions can successfully *induce* a change in behavior, whether these changes will *generalize* to real-life situations outside the clinic, and whether they will be *maintained* over a period of time. It appears that behavioral techniques can accomplish these goals in a great many cases, the professor concludes.

Bandura discounts the specter of a Machiavellian behavior therapist controlling and manipulating the attitudes and values of an unsuspecting client. "It is . . . not a question of imposing controls where none existed before," he says. "All behavior is inevitably controlled, and the operations of psychological laws cannot be suspended by romantic conceptions of human behavior," he adds. "The process of behavior change, therefore, involves substituting new controlling conditions for those that have regulated a person's behavior. The basic moral question is not whether man's behavior will be controlled, but rather by whom, by what means, and for what ends." As for aversion therapy, he asks, "Is it not far more humanitarian to offer the client a choice of undergoing a brief, painful experience to eliminate [for example] self-injurious behavior, . . . [rather than] enduring over many years the noxious, and often irreversible, consequences that will inevitably result if his behavior remains unaltered?"

In the end, since behavior modification is so result oriented, aversion therapy will rise or fall on its record of achievement. After a decade of beehive activity, that record is still unclear. There have been a large number of single-case successes reported along with a smaller number of failures. A lot of the studies are scientifically sloppy. There are few large-scale experiments with proper controls, comparisons, and follow-ups. So there are a large number of questions which have not been resolved satisfactorily. Among them:

● In the reported successes, has the follow-up time (usually six months to a year) been sufficient to catch the inevitable relapses? Some therapists say that if a patient has not relapsed after a year, it is likely he will stay "cured." Some put the time at two or five years, and one long-term study noted an increasing number of relapses with alcoholics through 10 years.

● Were the successful outcomes due to the aversive techniques themselves or to other factors? Indications are that a client's motivation, expectations, and the entire clinical atmosphere have some bearing on the outcome.

● What should be the relationship between therapist and client? Some therapists are deliberately brusque and have minimal patient contact so as not to "contaminate" the research results. Others say that a warm, caring attitude by the therapist is at least as important as the aversive techniques.

● Just how important is a client's motivation? Studies with court-referred cases show that the greater the external compulsion for seeking treatment, the less likely it is that therapy will be beneficial. But how strong should a self-referred client's motivation be and is there any way to measure it?

● What is the effect on therapists and others who administer aversion therapy? Psychologists agree it is unpleasant for them, and one British male nurse urges his colleagues to be on the lookout for any sadistic tendencies they might harbor.

● What is the effect on therapists and others who administer aversion therapy? Psychologists agree it is unpleasant for them, and one British male nurse urges his colleagues to be on the lookout for any sadistic tendencies they might harbor.

● Should certain kinds of aversive methods be used for particular kinds of problems? Many therapists think the technique should be "appropriate" for the target behavior. Thus an alcoholic or overeater would be made nauseous while a patient with uncontrollable impulses to pull his hair would be shocked. But at least one clinician warns that if the technique has too close a relationship to the problem, it will not be effective.

● How intense should the punishment be? Answers range all over the ball park from "barely perceptible" to "shock the hell out of them." Each side cites statistics and theories to back up its view.

● How long should the therapy continue after the problem appears eliminated? More than a few therapists have conceded that they ended treatment and closed cases at the first sign of success, which was too soon. Others continue for several more treatments to try to ensure that "overlearning" takes place.

● Are periodic "booster" sessions a good idea? They have become more in vogue and an increasing number of therapists regularly program them at the time of the initial session.

● Is there any way to tell in advance whether a particular patient will benefit from aversion therapy? Two psychologists working with homosexuals believe they have identified several predictive factors based on personality and other tests, but the results are open to question.

● Are there any people who definitely should not undergo aversive conditioning? On physiological grounds, cardiac patients and those with gastrointestinal problems should almost always be excluded. The answer is not clear from a psychological standpoint.

● What are the side effects of aversion therapy? In the short term, some aggression, depression, and physiological problems have cropped up. Therapists claim that these disappear in a week or two at the most. No studies have specifically zeroed in on possible long-term effects.

● Should punishment techniques be used alone or only in conjunction with other methods of behavior therapy? The consensus now seems to be that additional methods must accompany aversion to provide a new, alternate behavior pattern. There is not unanimous agreement on this point.

● If a patient *knows* he is not going to be shocked away from the clinic, how can the treatment work? Psychologists agree that the phenomenon, called *generalization*, does indeed work in many, but not all, cases. One explanation is that external stimuli (such as the smell of alcohol) trigger in the mind symbolic associations with the therapy and help to reinforce the effects of the treatment. This also would happen when the patient voluntarily recalls the therapy.

● Finally, if aversion therapy really works, how and why does it work?

In trying to answer that last question, most psychologists now discount a simple mechanical conditioning theory (as with Pavlov's dogs) for a more complex explanation. Using the alcoholic as an example, this view holds that the painful stimulus (the shock) causes both a general emotional arousal (fear, anxiety, or repugnance) and an instinctive escape and withdrawal response. These are usually incompatible with the alcoholic behavior and therefore capable of replacing it, at least temporarily. Since the entire chain of behavior leading to drinking was punished, any links in that chain (thinking about drinking, approaching a bar, and so on) would also arouse emotional reactions for some time after the actual punishment had taken place. The aversive techniques might also set up an internal cue or early warning system, blinking brightly to help a person remain aware of his behavior at all times. The punishment, then, would function as some sort of crutch to help a person kick a habit he really wants to give up.

In addition, any responses that ended the punishment or helped to avoid it are reinforced in real-life situations. Since these are also incompatible with alcoholic behavior, they give the patient some breathing space to build up nondrinking behavior patterns to supplant the alcoholism. Many psychologists feel this is essential, for without it the aversive aspects of the treatment will wear off in time and the problem will return, they say. What the therapy has done is to increase the patient's options.

•

There seem to be no limits to the weapons in the aversion therapist's arsenal. In addition to electric shock, a long list of nausea-producing drugs, and verbal aversion, there are breath holding, starvation, gunshots, white noise, hot air, ridicule, foul-tasting concoctions, and rubber bands, to name a few. Shock machines, the most popular method used today, range from do-it-yourself portable models to elaborate contrivances that sell for $1,500 or more. The latter have slide machine attachments and can be programmed to operate even without a therapist in the room. One of the largest manufacturers, the Farrall Instrument Company of Grand Island, Nebraska, takes a somewhat defensive attitude in its catalog which highlights a wireless shocker "useful on the playground and in similar situations." (The company's exhibit at one psychologists' convention was the focus of a noisy demonstration by a homosexual group that accused Farrall of "genocide against the gay community.") Farrall says that it looks on aversion therapy "as a superb tool to be used in conjunction with other types of more traditional therapy." The company adds that it is opposed to electric cattle prods (which it does not manufacture and which have been used particularly with mentally disturbed children) since "severe punishment works against the conditioning principles and produces hostility."

As of now there are no clear guidelines, no standards for aversion therapists to follow. For instance, most practitioners say that aversion therapy cannot work unless the patient is fully committed to changing his behavior and actively cooperates with the therapist. Therefore, they say, there is no ethical problem since the patient himself is making the choice. That may be true in many cases, but aversion therapy has been used with infants and retarded or brain-damaged patients who have little understanding of the process. It also has been used against the wills of people (particularly prisoners) or without patients' prior knowledge. One psychologist, Ronald P. Gruber, suggests that this is the best way to administer the punishment cure. He cites with approval a case in which two Japanese therapists gave a nausea drug to alcoholics without telling them. Results were supposedly "excellent"; since the patients were unaware of the reason for their nausea, they stopped drinking even outside the clinic. That conclusion seems far fetched, and the ethics involved indefensible.

In 1969 British psychologists Stanley Rachman and John Teasdale published a lengthy monograph covering their own and others' work with aversion therapy. They view the treatment with mixed feelings. "On the one hand, we are interested in it as a psychological process and welcome the introduction of effective treatment methods," they write. "On the other hand, we recognize that it is an unpleasant form of therapy and one which is open to abuse." Aversion should be offered to patients only if all other methods fail and after they carefully weigh the matter and give their consent, the psychologists caution. "Our evaluation of the available evidence is that aversion therapy is probably effective—but we have been unable to satisfy ourselves beyond all doubt," Rachman and Teasdale conclude. There has been little in the past few years to change that view. The jury is still out.

Chapter II

WELCOME TO
DUFFY'S TAVERN

Mary sits quietly in the small closet of a room that affectionately has been dubbed "Duffy's Tavern." A slight smile creases her round face as she flicks her bangs across her forehead, only to have them spring back again. Absentmindedly she tugs at the hem of her summery housedress, already in place well below her knees. She glances around the now familiar room with a calm but expectant look. Bottles of vodka and scotch, gin and bourbon, rye and rum line the shelves and a short platform like so many glass soldiers. Two quarts of Smirnoff vodka, Mary's favorite tipple, stand guard in front, casting a long shadow in the overhead light.

The soothing whitewashed walls of the cubicle are splashed here and there with slick, colorful magazine advertisements cleverly inveigling "Dry a Martini Tonight," or pushing "The Drink That Ends the Day and Begins the Evening," or pitching subliminally, "Scotch and the Single Girl." Mary does not need the boost from Madison Avenue. For the last 10 of her 34 years the soft-spoken nun has been an alcoholic. Now, she hopes, with the help of shocks and chemically induced nausea, she is about to hop up on the wagon for

17

good and leave the nightmare world of alcoholism far behind.
The odds are not greatly in her favor.

•

There are some 5 million hard-core alcoholics in the
United States. Another 4 million are "problem drinkers." Alcoholics and problem drinkers have trouble handling life.
There's a lot of disagreement among professionals over just
what alcoholism is, what its causes are, and, of course, how to
handle it. Most definitions are long and complex. Clinically
speaking, alcoholism is a dependence on booze, for whatever
reason. Practically, "alcoholism is sadness," as one madman
reveals to another in Frederick Exley's novel, A Fan's Notes.

For years alcoholics were looked on as a sinful lot: weak,
unworthy people who gave in to Demon Rum. It was not until
1970 that the American College of Physicians issued an official edict proclaiming alcoholism a disease—one that shortens
the chronic alcoholic's life span by 10 to 12 years and costs
the United States some $25 billion a year in lost work time
and related health and welfare expenses. There is now solid
evidence that even though alcoholism certainly does harm the
body, the problem is not really similar to a disease such as
tuberculosis or cancer. There are many different causes of
alcoholism, just as there are many different types of personali-
ties, and a large number of researchers are convinced that
alcoholism is behaviorally linked.

Alcohol has powerful properties to reduce stress, tran-
quilize, or even reduce boredom. Reduced tension can be a
strong enough "reward" to maintain excessive drinking habits. Once the alcoholic becomes *physically* dependent, he has
to continue swilling great quantities to avoid the painful and
noxious effects of withdrawal. But why do some people put in
stressful situations become alcoholics while others abstain
entirely or remain what we call "social" drinkers? There are,
of course, physical differences and levels of tolerance. A greater factor seems to be the learning that takes place in childhood
and adolescence when a person picks up patterns of behavior
from family, friends, and associates. As he grows older, the

drinker may be positively rewarded by camaraderie or success in business deals when he belts down a bunch with the boys.

•

Patrick Frawley has his own explanation of alcoholism. The white-haired self-made millionaire (Papermate pens, Schick safety razors, Technicolor) and champion of conservative causes is not a psychologist and does not have any medical background. He is a former alcoholic, however, and in the last 10 years he and the business organizations he controls have spent some $6 million, by his own estimate, to try to come up with a "cure" for alcoholism. For years his medical task force tried to develop a drug to solve the problem. The scientists finally gave up and went back to the treatment that helped Frawley in 1963, one that revolves around aversion therapy.

"I knew I wasn't an alcoholic because I was a philanthropist," Frawley says, his eyes piercing an interviewer one moment, then staring off into space. Pat Frawley is a big man with boundless energy which he sometimes has trouble keeping under control. He jumps up, paces around, punches a fist into his hand for emphasis. He *knows* he has the answers and sounds sincere when he says that he did not start Schick Laboratories to make a pile of money, but to help millions of suffering alcoholics and, later, smokers. If everything he says does not quite make sense, it could be because Frawley has told his story so many times, always using the same phrases and the same anecdotes, that he assumes he already has said it or you already have heard it.

Frawley has picked up and expanded on one theory of alcoholism that had some brief popularity in the 1960s, and which today is looked on as just one of scores of interesting but unproven hypotheses. It is a theory of genetic susceptibility, that certain ethnic and national groups are more likely to become alcoholics than others. If the theory happens to fit in with Frawley's own personal bout with alcoholism, so much the better.

Frawley is showing some people around the Schick Alco-

hol Treatment Unit of St. Vincent's Hospital in Los Angeles,
bumps into an interviewer and insists on giving him the
"whole story" firsthand. The way Frawley explains, it all has
to do with climate and kidneys. The kidneys of people whose
ancestors lived in areas of the world where water was always
plentiful developed so that their main function was to cycle
water out of the body, not to purify it. People from the desert
areas have kidneys whose primary task is to recycle water.
When the desert types get thirsty, they tend to get drowsy and
slow down, thus conserving body water. But when a wetlander gets thirsty, he panics, because he always has had plenty
of water available over the millennia, Frawley says. But what
does all that have to do with alcoholism? Well, Frawley continues a mile a minute, alcohol is a diuretic and causes the
body to lose water, and when you lose water, you get thirsty.
The wetlander (like the Eskimos, the Indians, and the Irish) is
more likely to panic and drink a lot and therefore get addicted
to alcohol, he adds.

"Look," Frawley frets. "I'm of Irish ancestry, right? Well,
the other day we had a cocktail party at my house and I had
five Seven-Ups and pineapple juice. Before I was cured, I
would drink half a dozen or more scotch and sodas like they
were lemonade. It's the thirst that does it, the thirst."

Pat Frawley, like many alcoholics, did not think he was
one. "I thought I was good at drinking. And I didn't have any
problems that led me to drink. But every couple of months
there'd be these embarrassing little incidents and finally my
wife convinced me to try Shadel, although I didn't know what
I was getting into. It was in Seattle so I thought they just took
you for a walk in the North Woods and told you to behave
yourself."

The Shadel Sanatorium, a low, sprawling building set
amidst a grove of tall trees in a suburb of Seattle, was founded
in 1935 for the sole purpose of treating alcoholics. For two
decades it was practically the only place to use aversion therapy after the treatment had fallen out of favor elsewhere. It
was at Shadel that aversive techniques were refined and that
one of the most thorough follow-up studies of people treated
with aversion therapy was carried out in the late 1940s.

Schick, which no longer is connected with the safety razor people, still incorporates the results of that study in its claims of success, although today's methods have evolved quite a ways from those employed earlier at the sanatorium.

•

Alcoholic beverages have been around since before recorded history, and so have excessive drinkers. Attempts to use aversive techniques to fight the problem apparently have been with us nearly as long, well before Pavlov conditioned a dog to salivate to a bell. One common method was to place spiders or other creepy things in with the wine or mead. An old Russian folk cure to end drunkenness was to add a concoction made from the roots of the hazelwort plant to the drink of an unsuspecting sot. It caused the drinker to vomit and therefore sober up, but like the spiders it did not stop the alcoholic from going back for more the next time. As a report from the National Institute on Alcohol Abuse and Alcoholism notes, alcoholics in the past have been admonished, scolded, denounced, jailed, beaten, dunked, lashed, and threatened with eternal damnation, but there is no evidence that any of these certainly aversive techniques ever reformed any chronic heavy drinker.

One of the earliest cited cases of the use of an aversive technique on humans, based on Pavlov's work, was in the Soviet Union in the late 1920s where the problem was—as it remains today—an unrequited love affair with vodka. A Russian researcher named N. V. Kantorovich treated a group of 20 alcoholics by pairing cards printed with the words "vodka," "wine," and "beer" with electric shocks, giving additional shocks for the actual sight, smell, and taste of the beverages. Kantorovich reported that 14 of the group were totally abstinent when checked at periods ranging from 3 weeks to 20 months. Out of a similar group of 10 alcoholics who received only hypnotic suggestion and some medication, all but one had reverted to excessive drinking within a few days of discharge from the hospital, the Russian reported.

Kantorovich's findings were largely ignored, surprising

in one respect because, over the years, the proven success rates for various methods of "curing" alcoholics have been abysmally low. Because of the lack of well-researched studies to provide a basis for comparison, most of the figures used today are broad estimates. The evidence indicates that certain alcoholics might be helped by one method and not another, so the problem is to predict in advance which method to try on which alcoholic. There is also a broad question of how to define success. Traditionally it has meant total abstinence, but a number of researchers now believe that many alcoholics can be turned into controlled, "social drinkers." And does abstinence really mean anything without corresponding improvements in other areas of the ex-alcoholic's life? The uncertainties are compounded by the bitter backbiting in the alcoholism research field, with investigators who have put all their life work and reputations into one basket jealously guarding it, while trying to tip over the basket of the kid down the street. For most treatments, the highest claims of success are around 20 to 30 percent; between 5 to 10 percent of heavy drinkers become abstinent without any kind of treatment.

•

The initial work at Seattle's Shadel Sanatorium was carried out by a team of doctors led by Walter L. Voegtlin, Shadel's chief of staff and research director, and Frederick Lemere, a consulting psychiatrist. The purpose of the Shadel treatment was to create an aversion to every facet of alcoholic beverages: their sight, taste, smell, and even thoughts about them. Basically the method was to make patients nauseous and vomit alcoholic drinks by giving them a shot of a drug known as emetine. There would be about four to six treatment sessions lasting up to an hour each during a normal 10-day stay at the sanatorium. The alcoholics (by now, hopefully, ex-alcoholics) would come back for one or two reconditioning sessions anytime their desire to drink returned or, to play it safe, at six months and a year after the first set of treatments.

What is apparently the last detailed evaluation of the

Shadel program to be published appeared in June, 1950. After eliminating the few hundred patients who refused conditioning therapy and several hundred more who could not be tracked down for a follow-up check, Shadel claimed that 44 percent of 4,096 clients remained totally abstinent after their first treatment. Adding in a number of successfully reconditioned patients, that total increased to a respectable 51 percent for a 13-year period ending in 1948. The overall cure rate, however, was bolstered by a proportionately larger number of men and women who were treated toward the end of the study. A further analysis of the data shows that 60 percent of the former alcoholics remained abstinent for at least one year, 51 percent for at least two years, sliding down to 38 percent for at least five years and 23 percent for at least ten years after their first treatment. The real test of the therapy, then, comes sometime after the first year.

A further note of caution should be raised. For one thing, despite the fact that some patients were eliminated from treatment at the outset because of physical disabilities, at least three deaths were considered to be the direct result of treatment—one from congestive heart failure and two from coronary occulsion. At least four other patients died from delirium tremens (the DTs) during or after withdrawal. Delirium causes the alcoholic to become confused and brings on horrifying hallucinations. It leads to trembling, fever, and sometimes convulsions; about 5 percent of alcoholics who go through the DTs while hospitalized die and about 20 to 25 percent who suffer delirium alone die as a result.

The Shadel researchers also point out that they had something of a select group, what might be called the alcoholic "elite." First, the patients were all voluntary, although often under pressure from family or employers. Since the cost of treatment then was between $450 and $750, the patients were also "sufficiently stable and productive to be able to pay this amount" or could at least convince someone else that they were worth the stake. Results with 100 charity patients were discouraging.

"Circumstances indicate that we automatically get a high

percentage of prognostically favorable patients for treatment and that the atmosphere of the institution is conducive to full cooperation on the part of the patient," Voegtlin and Lemere said. "We believe that the conditioned-reflex treatment is of value primarily for the advantageously circumstanced type of alcoholic patient. It probably does not offer much hope to the inadequate, skid-row type and is inapplicable to those alcoholics who do not admit their problem or, if they do, refuse to make an effort to help themselves."

The Shadel researchers also found that a number of other factors seemed to be tied to their overall "cure" rate. The most successful clients were apt to be those over 35 years old, married with few family problems, steadily employed, in the middle or upper class economically, and living in a small community. Also, they did not have police records, were not inherently nervous, and did not have physical handicaps or suffer delirium during or after withdrawal. It also appeared that the longer a patient drank before seeking assistance, the better his chance was of remaining abstinent, although paradoxically those who had remained abstinent on their own prior to treatment also had a higher rate of abstinence following treatment. Especially cooperative patients and those who regularly attended sessions of "abstinence clubs" made up of former Shadel patients (sort of a junior Alcoholics Anonymous) also had substantially higher abstinence rates than the average.

•

When Patrick Frawley went to Shadel in 1963, he was immediately impressed with both the staff and the treatment. "All it took was the first hour," he recalls. "I went through the nausea business and I said, 'My God, I've been drinking all this? Oh, my poor wife!' You see, the main problem is that people don't realize they're excessive drinkers. It's just like chain smoking, only a lot more humiliating. The main problem is accepting the fact that you need treatment. Look, I always thought I was good at drinking. And, my God, I was an alcoholic! Well, we've all been misled that alcohol addiction is tied to badness. An alcoholic has always been looked at as a bum, but that's all changing now." In order to push that change along a little faster, Frawley bought the Shadel Sanatorium, poured money into the fruitless research for a drug to cure alcoholism then opened two more Schick alcoholism treatment units in Fort Worth, Texas, and Los Angeles.

•

As Mary, the nun with the fondness for Smirnoff, found out recently, the Schick method has changed considerably from the early days at Shadel when treatment consisted of nothing but chemically induced nausea.

It is a little after 8 A.M. as the sun makes a valiant effort to pierce through the heavy Los Angeles smog and brighten the small lounge in the separate, 20-bed Schick ward at St. Vincent's Hospital. Mary looks bright and alert as she sits on a long, overstuffed sofa awaiting the first event of the day. Next to her, fighting a losing battle against a massive dose of tranquilizers, a housewife named Theresa, who is in her forties but whose face is so lined and baggy that she looks 10 years older, keeps nodding off, occasionally landing on Mary's right shoulder. In contrast to the nun, everything about Theresa seems shopworn: her faded blue housecoat, her frowsy gray hair, even her spirit.

Then, in struts a burst of energy in the form of Dr. Robert B. Dunn, clinic director and a member of Frawley's team since 1969. Bob Dunn has a small, compact body and knows how to clothe it in well-tailored suits, wide ties, and high-heeled patent leather shoes. He starts right in on his weekly lecture. It is always the same, and Mary has heard it before, but Dr. Dunn believes it bears constant repetition. Mary takes notes.

"Well, ladies, I'm going to explain what alcoholism is according to our view. Now, where can alcohol be found? Mary? That's right. Beer, wine, and spirits." To emphasize his points, Dr. Dunn writes the words on a blackboard and produces a bottle of cheap wine, a fifth of bourbon, and a can of beer. It is like a lecture to a high school chemistry class as Dr.

Dunn passes around a vial of ethyl alcohol and starts to explain addiction.

"There are three parts to it: physical dependence, tolerance, and psychic dependence. The first two are pretty simple to deal with. Physical withdrawal usually takes about two to four days here, although it could take up to two weeks." Mary nods in agreement; Theresa, who is still undergoing withdrawal, just nods.

"Psychic dependence. Ah, that's the crook of the whole thing." Now Dr. Dunn is really rolling. It is as though he is leading a revival meeting for alcoholics, and, in fact, he probably is. "What's the cause of alcoholism? Well for years we've heard that the roots of alcoholism were deep, dark psychiatric problems. Baloney! The *cause* is simply the interaction of the person and the drug. People drink for many reasons, but one of them is that they get some underlying pleasure or satisfaction. It makes it easier to tolerate stress or depression.

"Alcohol is simply *imprinted* with a positive image. It becomes an automatically learned subconscious behavior. And there are patterns. Listen, 85 percent of our patients have family histories of alcoholism. And the ethnic groups: 85 percent of male American Indians who use alcohol get addicted, and also other native groups like the Irish. But I've never had a Jewish patient; they're just not addicted. So some part of the susceptibility must be hereditary." To his credit, Dr. Dunn does not try to upstage Pat Frawley's wetlander versus desert-type diagnosis.

"What we have to do to cure psychic dependency," Dr. Dunn adds, "is to start with the 'plus' that alcohol has in your mind, add on a strong minus, and come up a zero. We're going to put a negative image of alcohol in your brains. We'll make drinking produce displeasure. And one of the most unpleasant things that we can think of, up to killing the patient," he chuckles in an aside, "is to produce nausea and associate it immediately with things tied to drinking." Dr. Dunn pauses for a moment to greet John, a middle-aged businessman with graying temples, who enters the room in his bathrobe, ready for a two-day stay for reconditioning. John has not had a drink for six months. Dr. Dunn wraps up his lecture in a few minutes and then takes a visitor on a tour of the clinic.

"You know we can't eliminate alcoholism completely," he confides. "But we can reduce psychic dependency during their 10-day stay here. If we could keep them for six months or a year, we could fix it so an alcoholic wouldn't even be able to look at an ad for alcohol without getting violently sick. The mind can be controlled that much."

Mary is ensconced in a small room off one of the main corridors of the ward. In front of her is a shelf with a small sink. A small electrode is attached to her right forearm with the wires leading to an outer room where Mel Clapp, her therapist, is watching her through a two-way mirror and rapidly pressing a key on a shock generator that makes the machine light up like a firefly in heat. Clapp knows what Mary is feeling. The former air force B-52 bomber pilot is also a former alcoholic who had gone through the Schick program three years previously. Clapp's experiences as a chronic and excessive drinker far outweighed his lack of psychological training. "You don't have to have special qualifications to do behavior modification," he says softly, snuffing out his fifth or sixth cigarette in a handy ashtray.

This is Mary's fourth session with the shock machine, and she has just about had her fill. She glances aimlessly at the bottles of Smirnoff, beer, and Seven-Up in front of her.

"Okay, Mary, now pick up the Smirnoff's," Mel coaxes.

"I don't even want to touch the vodka, Mel. Just the thought makes me nauseous."

Mel smiles. That's the hoped-for reaction. "Now Mary, pick up the beer and pour yourself some."

"Do I have to finish the beer?"

"Well, I'd like to get some more reactions."

As Mary picks up the beer, as she pours it, and as she swishes it around in her mouth, she receives a constant barrage of painful but not unbearable shocks (the level being predetermined with her cooperation). Mary's hand jerks spasmodically and she sets down the glass, spits out the beer, and reaches for a sip of Seven-Up.

"Very good, Mary, very good. That Seven-Up tastes real good, doesn't it?" Mel asks. Since there are no shocks or tension involved, it tastes like nectar from Mount Olympus. The soft drink is there to teach Mary a substitute behavior for that of drinking alcohol. "Okay, Mary you know what to do now."

"Yeah, pour it out." Mary is red and sweating profusely and her stomach is doing flip-flops as she spills out the rest of the beer.

"Now that feels real good, doesn't it?" Mel purrs, proud of his student.

When Mary entered the clinic eight days before, she had been ready to start treatment. Others have been drinking heavily and the first order of business is to dry them out, often by giving them gradually smaller amounts of alcohol and lots of sedatives. Patients also are given physical exams and told graphically just what alcohol abuse has done to their bodies. "You don't scare people out of behaviors no matter how bad off they are," Dr. Dunn says. "But it's important for them to know why we do what we do." All patients are given a thorough explanation of the treatment before it starts. Still, the first trip to "Duffy's Tavern" can be a harrowing experience.

The room, with four or five cases of liquor on display, is barely large enough to maneuver in. The patient sits in a hard-backed chair next to a large aluminum bowl about 2 feet across and is given an injection of an emetine-pilocarpine-ephedrine mixture to make him sweat, flush, and become anxious. In about seven minutes, just prior to the onset of the nausea, the patient gets a glass of his favorite alcoholic beverage mixed with water and has to smell it, taste it, and then swallow it. As soon as the drug takes effect, the patient is forced to drink as much as he can as rapidly as possible; this usually involves four to six drinks over a half-hour period, with the patient vomiting in between. Dr. Dunn explains that the vomiting is necessary so the patient will not retain any alcohol in his system (which would reduce the effectiveness of the aversive experiences). This parrots real-life situations in which a person becomes sick from drinking too much.

The clinic also has available a slide projector hooked to a

shock machine. When pictures of whiskey or other alcohol-related scenes appear on the screen, the patient can be shocked. He gets relief from the shock when a "normal" scene such as a family dinner is portrayed. In addition, Schick uses covert sensitization by having the alcoholic imagine distressing consequences for a drinking scene. "I don't think there's a technique that we don't use," Dr. Dunn says proudly. "It's hard to overdo this when you have them for just 10 days."

In those 10 days each patient normally receives 5 days of aversion treatments—one every other day. On off days Schick uses another method pioneered at the Shadel clinic: interviews under the influence of a drug made famous in spy stories as "truth serum." Patients receive intravenously a mixture of sodium pentothal and sodium amytal which, for about 40 minutes, puts them in a deeply sedated state just short of sleep. The purpose of the "interview" is to get the patient relaxed enough so he will talk freely about emotional or other factors that are contributing to his drinking problem. This enables the doctors to make a "quickie" psychiatric diagnosis instead of spending the weeks or months that are often required, they say. The medication also relieves the nervous tension that often leads to excessive drinking, and former patients who feel tension building up often come back for "booster shots," Dr. Dunn says. The therapists also give hypnoticlike suggestions against drinking and find out if the aversive treatments are working by asking the patient direct questions.

Schick also uses what it calls a "new life management program." In this the alcoholic is asked to change his lifestyle if it is tension or anxiety producing. There is relaxation training using intramuscular injections of barbiturates and tranquilizers, nutritional advice, group therapy, daily educational sessions, exercise and occupational therapy, and private counseling. "We have to give the patient a substitute for his alcoholic behavior," Dr. Dunn explains. "He has to know how to handle his problems without resorting to alcohol. We feel every time we add another method, we increase the overall effectiveness of the program. If we see that something isn't working, then we take it out."

The cost of the Schick program varies according to location. The basic treatment fee is at least $735 but with hospitalization and other costs the final bill in Los Angeles would be at least $2,300. Patients return for two-day reinforcement sessions (aversion and pentothal) in one month, three months, six months, and possibly a year if they still have any urge to drink. Dr. Dunn says that some 20,000 patients have been treated by the Schick-Shadel method and that 50 percent have remained abstinent after four years. "And there's no doubt that the lives of the other 50 percent are better, because what we've done is spoil drinking for them, and few go back to their previous depths," he says.

The Schick claims to success are open to some questioning. As late as 1972, Dr. Dunn told a meeting of a section of the Texas Medical Association that "data from Schick's hospital in Seattle, which has used nausea aversion and pentothal modalities for years, report a total sobriety rate of 51 percent in 4,468 cases collected over 14 years. Smaller series average 63 percent abstinence." Although Dr. Dunn acknowledged that it was too early to determine the effectiveness of the expanded Schick program, he neglected to mention that the figures he cited were collected 24 years previously. There has not been any comparable study published since.

The Schick people are sensitive to criticism about their use of aversion therapy. "Sure we're brainwashing—but for the good of people," Dr. Dunn insists. "It does the job—probably the only consistently proven way to do it. You know, I think of it as being like fire; it's the most effective thing for heating people—or burning them. You can make anything look bad by putting it in a bad perspective. We'd certainly want to keep aversion therapy in the right hands."

Alex Reuss, president of Schick Laboratories, agrees that aversion therapy can be misused and is becoming somewhat faddish. "We saw A Clockwork Orange too," he says. "It was stupid, absurd. It's just not legitimate or accurate to compare us to that." Adds Dr. James W. Smith, chief of staff at the Seattle operation: "Some people object to what we do as un-American. Well, in reality we're giving a person back his freedom of choice; we make it possible for an addict not to drink. As for the complaint that we're hurting people or making them uncomfortable, you have to realize that what we're dealing with here is a fatal illness. Not to intervene is even more harmful than to intervene this way."

•

There were a few scattered experiments, mostly in Europe, around the time that Shadel started its treatment program. Later many European therapists tried an aversion therapy method using a nausea-producing narcotic, apomorphine, that also was used by itself in treating alcoholics. Apomorphine sessions continued practically around the clock at two- to four-hour intervals until the therapists were convinced that an aversion toward all types of alcoholic beverages had been achieved. The Shadel doctors tried apomorphine, but rejected it because they said its nausea-inducing quality is too short-lived for effective conditioning and its sedative action interferes with treatment. It also led to severe shock reactions in a number of cases. The Europeans, on the other hand, rejected Shadel's use of emetine because it produces severe fatigue.

Classical aversion therapy took a back seat in the 1950s to the new "miracle cure" of disulfiram, better known by one of its trade names, Antabuse. People who took Antabuse had sharply aversive physical reactions when they later drank even a little alcohol. First, there would be a disagreeable warmth and flushing of the face along with heart palpitations, followed by a headache, dizziness, vomiting, weakness, and all the other symptoms of a first-rate hangover—lasting for one to two hours. All in all, an unpleasant and quite averse reaction, but unlike the claims for classical aversion therapy, backers of Antabuse did not contend that the drug eliminated alcoholic behavior. It had to be taken constantly (in some cases it was implanted under the skin). Originally, test doses were administered under clinical supervision followed by alcohol, to impress upon the alcoholic the serious consequences of any future drinking. Some therapists claimed the test doses were essential, but treatment centers started abandoning them as reports filtered in of unpredictable, severe, and sometimes even fatal results. A number of other potentially serious side effects from drinking even moderate amounts of alcohol while on Antabuse became apparent, including gastrointestinal disturbances and reduced sexual potency. A few researchers suggested that the specific effects of the drug were not really necessary, and, in fact, it was really the motivation for abstinence and the day-by-day discipline that led to any successes. One Russian study concluded that 150 alcoholics treated with a placebo sugar pill did as well as 150 using Antabuse. Although the drug still has its partisans, as do two similar drugs (citrated calcium cyanamide and metronidazole), there is not much enthusiasm for any of the three today.

Hypnosis also has been tried. In early practice, alcoholics were given posthypnotic suggestions that their arms would become paralyzed whenever they tried to take a drink. As Albert Bandura, the Stanford University psychologist, observes: "This mode of therapy not only resulted in a considerable amount of spilt liquor, but also fostered the acquisition of highly ingenious drinking styles." After refining the technique, some therapists reported success in hypnotically inducing aversion to alcoholism. The alcoholic is hypnotized, then told to relive vividly his worst hangover, and when he starts to recall the nausea and vomiting, he is asked to smell and taste alcoholic beverages. The client is also given direct suggestions that the taste or smell of alcohol will produce similarly disagreeable reactions in the future.

By the early 1960s, as behavior therapy methods began to gain some respectability, therapists went back to chemical and electric aversive treatments. Under those broad categories, many different methods are bunched, and each group has its adherents. Basically, those who favor chemicals say that since alcohol is so involved with smell and taste, nausea is the proper negative stimulus for the specific problem at hand. Those who favor electric shock treatment say the method can be much better controlled and regulated, thus increasing the chances for successful conditioning to take place.

One of the most questionable alcohol aversion treatments originated in the early 1960s in Canada (later duplicated in Iowa and Illinois). Though it did not provoke much criticism at the time, similar treatment of troublesome inmates at two California prisons a few years later unleashed a storm of protest, as we will see in a later chapter.

The method was devised by three professors at Queen's University in Kingston, Ontario—Dugal Campbell, S. G. Laverty and R. E. Sanderson. The professors were not impressed by the treatments employing emetine (Schick-Shadel) or apomorphine because, among other reasons, these drugs did not produce a sufficiently traumatic experience for the alcoholic. The Canadians hit on a solution: "One need, perhaps the basic need, for human life is the continuation of respiration. It seems axiomatic that a temporary inability to breathe, along with an inability to communicate this distress, must in the conscious human be a most terrifying experience."

The drug that they decided was sufficiently traumatic is best known by the trade names Scoline or Anectine. The drug is closely related to the vine extract that South American Indians have used for centuries to poison the tips of their arrows. Immediately following an injection of Scoline a person is completely paralyzed, his muscles feel like cream cheese, and he cannot move or breathe. The Canadians' technique was fairly simple. An alcoholic was placed on a stretcher in a small room and hooked up to a polygraph machine (or lie detector) that monitored four bodily functions including heartbeat and breathing. A salt water solution trickled into a vein in his left arm via a hypodermic needle.

After a patient acclimated himself to the situation, the researchers gave him a bottle with a snort of his favorite drink. He grabbed the bottle, sniffed it, tasted a little, then handed it back. After doing this five times in five minutes, the researchers injected 20 milligrams of Scoline into the vein instead of salt water. When initial reaction set in, the therapists handed the bottle back to the patient and, just before he lifted it to his lips, the full effects of Scoline hit like a freight train. The experimenters then put a few drops of the drink into the alcoholic's mouth, but took the bottle away as soon as signs of

regular breathing appeared. If the patient could be calmed
down enough, the experimenters attempted to have him repeat the look-smell sequence several times to determine any
changes in response.

This process, prima facie, raises serious doubts about the
moral and ethical basis for inflicting terror on people, even
"for their own good." Worse, it seems to lack any pretensions
to "voluntary" and "knowledgeable" consent. The subjects
were taken from the psychiatric ward of a general hospital
(in which most alcoholics traditionally end up to segregate
them from other patients) and from a mental hospital run by
Ontario. Most of the latter patients were not seeking treatment
for their alcoholism and several initially refused to take part
in the experiment. Furthermore, the researchers admit that
most of their subjects had chosen hospitalization as an alternative to prison, and many agreed to participate in hopes that
it would lead to a reduction of what they looked on as a
"sentence."

Three patients were not told anything except that they
would undergo a "frightening but harmless experience." Others were told simply that a "chemical change" would be produced that might help them later if they wanted to stop
drinking. They were also told the treatment was "unpleasant." From the brief case histories released by the experimenters, it is clear that many subjects had serious emotional
problems in addition to drinking. Several had contemplated
or actually tried suicide. Asked later to describe their Scoline
sensations, most patients said they had been convinced they
were dying.

Just as the effects of Scoline are unpredictable, results of
the experiment were inconclusive, the researchers admitted.
They claimed abstinence in 6 of the 15 alcoholics under their
care, but didn't say whether that was one week or one year
after the experiment. Other patient reactions ranged from an
immediate "bender" after treatment to overwhelming anxiety
while filling a cigarette lighter or car radiator.

Possibly anticipating some criticism of their methods, the
same group of researchers, in follow-up experiments, gave
their subjects a complete description of what would happen

and had them sign a consent form. But the researchers concluded that the drug treatment was a relative failure. Worse, they noted some apparently long-term side effects. The researchers said that many of those who had been given Scoline had significantly increased tension and anxiety, which in some cases led to even heavier drinking and increased insomnia. Irritability and headaches also were reported. "Punishment is a relatively ineffective means of modifying behavior if the behavior has been associated with previous punishments," the Canadians concluded. "This is certainly true of many heavy drinkers who have had opportunities to become habituated to the aversive effects of alcohol."

Still, two psychiatrists and a psychologist in Iowa City, Iowa, tried a similar method with 25 "volunteer alcoholics" at the Iowa City Psychopathic Hospital. John Clancy, P. Campbell, and research associate E. Vanderhoof were convinced the treatment was "economical" and had wide application with little risk. The researchers charitably informed their patients that if they had a reaction, their muscles would become weak and they would have "some difficulty in breathing." The patients were also told they might have a reaction in the future if they tried to drink or even smell alcoholic beverages; hence 14 potential subjects refused treatment. Once again, there was little difference between those patients who were given the drug and those who were not.

Another Scoline experiment using 12 patients at the Galesburg State Research Hospital in Galesburg, Illinois, also had dismal results, with only two successes a year after treatment, and one of the failures reported violent reactions to hair spray and mouthwash, among other things. In none of these Scoline experiments is there any indication that the researchers made an attempt to undo some of the problems they had wrought.

•

Chemical aversion therapy has been used in a number of Communist countries. A recent book by two leading experts on alcoholism in the Soviet Union titled *Klinika Alkogolizma* does not give the method very high marks. The authors claim that aversion treatment is not stable and speculate this might be because nausea and vomiting are a natural effect of drunkenness and therefore cannot do the trick. However, since the late 1950s the Institute on Alcoholism in Belgrade, Yugoslavia, has been treating alcoholics with aversion using a combination drug that provokes sweating, nausea, and vomiting. In its six-week treatment, the institute couples the drug with suggestion therapy. The therapist tells the alcoholic he will vomit as soon as he tastes some alcohol, while a tape recorder plays the haunting refrain of the alcoholic's own recorded statement: "Whenever I see alcohol or try to drink it, I will feel nausea and I will start vomiting." Out of 264 patients, the institute claims 136 were abstinent for at least 18 months. The drug used (antimonyl potassium tartrate) is lethal in relatively small doses, and the Yugoslavs urge caution. They also say that treatment must be combined with psychotherapy because the aversion affects only the alcoholic's readiness to drink, not the factors that make him an alcoholic.

Finally, a treatment that might be endorsed by Boris Karloff is recommended by William W. Gordon of the Gartloch Mental Hospital in Glasgow, Scotland. He acknowledges that "conditioning treatments, like psychotherapy, are really operations on the patients [although] no scalpel is used, no blood is shed." Seeking a treatment based on more "biologic principles" he came up with his own favorite mixture containing a drug called chloramphenicol, which, after a healthy dose of whiskey, he injected into a patient's mouth by means of syringes, tubes, and cheek clips. When the patient started to spit out the bitter mixture, he suddenly found himself over a basin filled with an ammonia solution that burnt his eyes, nose, and mouth so he was sure to vomit. Gordon later automated the process with a boxlike machine and ammonia gas injected directly into the alcoholic's mouth. The original mixture, however, did present some "disadvantages," he admits. For one, as little as 4.5 grams of chloramphenicol can be fatal. In Gordon's treatment alcoholics were given up to 14.2 grams of the drug over a two-week period. Since the mixture was spit out, Gordon theorized that only about 0.1 gram was left in the

alcoholic's mouth and that the "risks are probably small." Just
to be sure, however, he proposed to substitute something
called Bitrex (benzyldiethyl ammonium benate), which is
used industrially in the manufacture of cosmetics. Bitrex had
never before been used on humans, but Gordon got permission to do so and when last heard from was using it in a
solution which, he says, "appears harmless." He was even
contemplating increasing the dosage and possibly setting up
outpatient clinics using his automated device. In a long report
in the *American Journal of Psychotherapy*, Gordon goes on
for pages describing the technical details of his therapy. It
seems almost an afterthought when he notes that of 30 patients so treated, only 3 stopped drinking whiskey—and took
up beer. Some 16 others "could be fairly judged as improved," Gordon insists, based on a follow-up of only three
months.

•

With research results of chemical aversion therapy decid-
edly mixed, many therapists returned to Kantorovich's electric
shock. One of the first reports to attract attention appeared in
the *British Medical Journal* in January, 1964. R. J. McGuire
and M. Vallance, two Glasgow researchers, described how to
build a simple and cheap device powered by a 9-volt battery.
It administered shocks through electrodes attached to a soft
leather cuff around a patient's forearm. The shock strength
could be increased to the maximum the patient could bear and
the machine could be toted home so patients could administer
their own shocks. The researchers reported on only one alcoholic, a 48-year-old businessman still on the wagon six
months after treatment. He was shocked while sniffing test
tubes of whiskey and looking at cards symbolic of drinking
behavior.

Scotland, which for some unfathomable reason seems to
be a hotbed for such work, was the site of several other probes
into electric shock treatment for alcoholics. B. George Blake,
then a psychologist on the staff of Crichton Royal Hospital in
Dumfries, noted that even though shock treatment by itself

might lead to a temporary halt in drinking, the results probably were not permanent. "There is the possibility that the conditioned aversion response (drinking) may become extinguished while the drive, fear, or anxiety that motivates the drinking may remain unaltered," Blake added. Prior to shocking his patients, Blake taught them how to relax completely. The aversion therapy consisted of shocking the patient when he sipped a mixed drink and not ending the shock until he spit it out. Out of 37 patients, 17 were abstinent after one year and another five were listed as "improved."

Two other researchers in Aberdeen, Scotland, gave shocks at irregular intervals when a patient just sniffed alcohol and anticipated taking a drink; no drinking was allowed because, they said, such libations would rekindle the urge to drink despite painful electric shocks. The results were a total flop. The researchers found no differences between groups given aversion and psychotherapy and another engaged in a regular alcoholic ward routine.

Much of the current electric shock therapy is taking place in Veterans Administration hospitals all over the United States. The hospitals traditionally have a heavy case load of alcoholics under treatment. Peter Miller and Michel Hersen of the Veterans Administration Center in Jackson, Mississippi, have developed a way to measure drinking behavior both before and after aversive treatment. They have the alcoholic take part in a phony "taste test" in which he evaluates the taste of six different beverages. Three of the beverages are alcoholic and the researchers measure how much of these the patient drinks both before and after shock treatment. In a recent evaluation of their work with 30 chronic alcoholics, the researchers report no significant differences among groups treated with painful shocks, mild shocks, or group psychotherapy. They conclude that any success among aversion shock patients is due more to expectancy, therapist reinforcement, instructions, or the fact that treatment is an alternative to prison or a fine.

Robert S. Davidson, a psychologist at the Veterans Administration Hospital in Miami, Florida, is much more sanguine about the use of electric shocks to redirect alcoholics.

But his experiments with veterans raise important questions about where research and therapy end and unnecessary pain, some might even say torture, begins.

There are no established standards. Therapists using aversive shock agree that different patients have different tolerance levels, and that these levels may fluctuate. They agree on little else. Some believe that a barely discernible shock is effective; others use such words as "uncomfortable," "painful," or "barely tolerable." There have not been any reports of death or serious injury from aversive electric shock appearing in the psychological journals; there have not been very many cautions either.

One stark warning appears in a catalog of the former Lehigh Valley Electronics Company, now part of a division of Tech Serv in Beltsville, Maryland. When Lehigh Valley was acquired by Tech Serv, the company decided to drop all items associated with human shock. ("It's not a field we wanted to be involved in," a company official says.) The catalog concedes that "many conflicting statements about how much shock is lethal to humans have been made, some, below 1 millampere qualified by 'under certain circumstances' and others above levels known to cause burns." (The only recommended places for electrodes were the fingers of one hand or on the extremities or lower torso. At least one researcher, however, has reported using pulsing shock of 2 to 5 milliamperes applied directly to the heads of alcoholics for 30-second periods. This appears dangerous and totally unwarranted.)

Extrapolated from a welter of confusing statistics, the average maximum shock intensity seems to range from 2 to 8 milliamperes, with more cases in the lower end of the scale. One group of normal, healthy college students, for example, reported that 3 milliamperes was the maximum they could bear. Veterans Administration psychologist Robert Davidson disagrees. He increases the shock until he feels that all drinking behavior has been suppressed. The final shock level almost always exceeds the alcoholic's reported tolerance threshold. Davidson's patients must pull a lever 30 times to be "rewarded" with a small shot of their favorite drink and a shock. Out of a recent group of 23 patients, 13 completed the program and 6 received "a hair-frying" 40 milliamperes of electricity at one time or another, although their tolerance thresholds ranged from 0.13 to 7.75 milliamperes. Since 40 milliamperes was the maximum voltage Davidson could milk from his machine, it is not clear how much higher he would have gone, if at all, with a more powerful machine. As for the final 13 patients, Davidson reports that five were abstinent "except that two [of those] patients drank for one day only," after a six-month follow-up. However, even if all the original 23 patients became devout teetotalers and remained so for 10 years, the shock intensity seems hard to justify.

A far more humane method used on alcoholics is "covert sensitization," or verbal aversion therapy, in which the patient imagines drinking situations, becomes sick, and vomits. The technique is relatively new; although some initial results are encouraging, it needs more testing. Joseph R. Cautela of Boston College has pioneered in the whole area of covert conditioning, in which attempts are made to change a person's behavior through imagery rather than any actual physical processes. (The technique's use with other behavioral problems is detailed in later chapters.)

In any covert technique it is essential that the patient be able to picture vividly the scene suggested by the therapist and be able to recall it on cue. He is not simply seeing the situation; he actually is *in* it, suffering the aversive consequences as severely as those chemically or electronically induced. Although nausea and vomiting often are used as the aversive consequence, Cautela also has patients imagine a dentist drilling into their teeth, or snakes, spiders, and maggots crawling all over them. He alternates the aversive scene with a "relief" scene in which the patient imagines he has been offered alcohol, refused, and therefore feels strong and virtuous. Practicing lab scenes at home is essential; so is recalling the repugnant consequences every time the alcoholic is tempted to hoist the bottle. To break most alcoholic habits, Cautela believes, biweekly therapy sessions over a span of six months to a year are required. Interestingly, Cautela's methods ignore the taste of alcohol; they focus rather on punishing the intent to drink and all the little rituals that lead up to a snort. Other researchers in covert conditioning endorse periodic booster sessions. One even mails out printed versions of the aversive scenes to remind patients to practice at home.

•

One of the most encouraging developments in alcoholism research has evolved in just the last couple of years by redefining the problem at hand. For decades therapists insisted that total abstinence was the only measure of success. However, recent evidence indicates that many alcoholics who cannot stop completely can be taught to drink in a moderate, controlled way. "A return to controlled drinking is a more realistic form of behavior than abstinence in our alcoholic society in which most of the adult population drink with regularity," says Stanley Rachman, a respected clinical psychologist at the University of London's Institute of Psychiatry. "If our goal is controlled drinking, an occasional bout of excessive drinking need no longer be conceived of as a self-evident failure or 'relapse' but rather as a temporary loss of control."

Controlled drinking research is being carried out by a husband and wife psychologist team in California, Mark and Linda Sobell, and G. Terence Wilson, a psychologist with Rutgers University's Psychological Clinic in New Jersey. Both projects use aversive techniques as part of an overall program to help alcoholics, rather than depending on punishment alone as a cure. Their work has not been warmly received by hard-liners in alcoholism research. The Sobells say: "The majority of the few individuals who have dared to so much as suggest that alcoholics may be able to resume some sort of limited drinking after treatment have been the victims of invective, professional ostracism and other measures hardly appropriate as scientific discourse."

The Sobells' project at California's Patton State Hospital for treatment of alcoholism involved 70 male patients interviewed in advance to determine their treatment goal: abstinence or controlled drinking. At the start, the patients were given alcohol until they became drunk; the sessions were videotaped and replayed later for their educationally sobering effect. An electric shock generator was also used. Those who wanted to end up abstinent got shocked when placing an order and drinking. Those who wanted to become social drinkers got shocked only for such things as ordering a straight drink, taking a gulp rather than a sip, or ordering too much or too soon. Few electric shocks were administered during the course of treatment, but the Sobells believe the threat of the shocks was a big help. The patients, aided by the therapists, had to come up with nondrinking behavior in the kinds of situations that previously had led to the bottle.

In a two-year follow-up, those trying to become social drinkers and who underwent the special program functioned well for around 90 percent of all days, compared to a 45 percent rate for those who received normal hospital treatment. The abstinence seekers in the experimental program functioned well for around 65 percent of all days, compared to 45 percent for regularly treated patients.

At Rutgers, Wilson and an associate, Raymond C. Rosen, report on the case of Mr. V., a 30-year-old electrician who had been an alcoholic since the age of 18. His wife was about to divorce him and he had serious problems with his health and employment. Wilson says his immediate goal was "to win a breathing space" by at least temporarily decreasing Mr. V's drinking through aversion therapy. Following other researchers, he taught Mr. V. how to estimate his own blood level of alcohol and allowed him free rein with the bottle if he kept his level at a predetermined rate of sobriety. Any increase in the blood alcohol level resulted in painful shocks. Mr. V's drinking pattern changed from gulping down his drinks to sipping them leisurely while he chatted in a friendly manner with the two researchers.

Later, Mr. V's wife complained that while he might be limiting himself to the specified level, he was drinking practically every day. The researchers then used a method called "behavior rehearsal" to reproduce in the clinic some of the stressful situations that apparently led to drinking, thus teaching the man how to deal with these situations in real life. Mr.

V. was taught how to relax and also how to stop his thoughts about wanting to drink.

Finally, in order to maintain his new self-control, Mr. V. and his wife entered into a contract with the researchers which permitted drinking only when Mr. V. was in a good mood and in a social situation. He could drink only a maximum of four ounces of alcohol over a two-day period. A breach of the contract, which happened only once, led to a forfeiture of $10 (a lot of money for the financially hard-pressed couple) which was in the hands of the researchers. The money was sent in Mr. V's name to the organization he hated most, the Salvation Army, along with a letter commending the group on its work. Mr. V. had maintained his controlled drinking behavior for more than a year at last report. "Complex psychiatric disorders such as alcoholism," Wilson notes, "are usually controlled by several factors which must *all* be modified if lasting therapeutic benefit is to result."

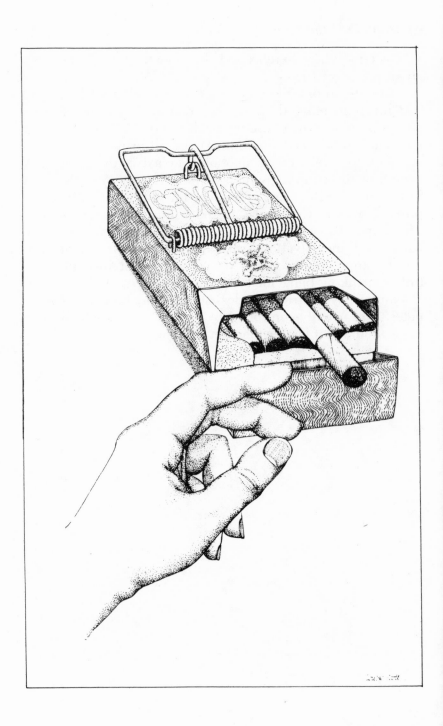

Chapter III

SMOKING THEM OUT

*Quitting smoking is the easiest thing in the world. I
ought to know. I've done it nine times.*

Will Rogers

You've come a long way baby.

Ubiquitous cigarette ad

Cigarette smoking seems, to nonsmokers, like a fairly
simple habit to kick. It is expensive, messy, foul, and unnatural, or no more natural than a cow inhaling burnt alfalfa.
Worse, the medical establishment proclaims it a serious danger to health and life itself. Realizing their folly, some 30
million smokers in the last half century have managed to kick
the habit completely. However, the American public fired up
a record 602 billion cigarettes in 1974, and smoking remains

45

such a tenacious process that millions of smokers have tried, failed, and are still walking that proverbial mile for their thin white tubes of pleasure.

In 1964, with much pomp and trappings, the surgeon general of the United States gave official sanction to what researchers had known for years: Cigarette smoking is linked to cancer, heart disease, respiratory disorders, and even many automobile accidents. On the average a young man who starts smoking two or more packs a day will live eight years less than his nonsmoking contemporary. Health warnings ("The Surgeon General Has Determined . . .") appear in fine print on every pack and carton and in every advertisement, adding an almost masochistic note for smokers already bombarded with what must be the biggest government propaganda campaign since war bonds. Tobacco moguls, who control an annual $10-billion-plus business in the United States alone, still insist that all the facts are not in, that it is too early to draw firm conclusions. Nonetheless, in a foot-dragging response to government pressure and consumer demand they have reduced tar and nicotine content in most brands and boosted the number of filter-tip cigarettes.

So what has actually happened? After a temporary downturn a few years ago, cigarette smoking is bigger than ever. Today at least 52 million Americans smoke regularly, a rise of 2 million since the surgeon general's first report. (Smokers are defined as people who have smoked at least 100 cigarettes in a lifetime.) Although 10 million people—mostly men—gave up smoking in the last 10 years, there have been enough new recruits to more than fill the gap. The National Clearinghouse for Smoking and Health reports that about 3,000 people a day take up cigarette smoking. Per capita consumption, which fell to below 4,000 cigarettes a year in 1969, rose to 4,130 in 1973, or more than half a pack a day for the average smoker. Most smokers want to quit—or so they say when pressed by friends and relatives—and many have tried to stop at least once. A recent Gallup poll for the American Cancer Society said that half of all adult Americans who smoke want to give it up. Those who most want to quit are under 50, better educated, and higher earners than their staunch-smoking counterparts, the poll revealed.

Some doctors are convinced that for most people, clinics and other types of therapy are a waste of time and money. "I believe only a small percentage of smokers will ultimately require . . . this kind of professional support to be successful," says Dr. Donald T. Frederickson, a New York heart and chest specialist. "Most individuals are perfectly capable of stopping smoking on their own once they have made a *decision* to stop." Dr. Frederickson adds that to make such a decision, the smoker must appreciate the "personal relevance" of the health threat. Most smokers have not made that crucial decision. It takes some mysterious trigger, which could go off at any time, for a smoker really to feel in his gut what he knows in his mind.

The "Smoker's Self-Testing Kit," published by the National Clearinghouse for Smoking and Health, says, in effect: You must be aware that smoking is an *important* problem, that it has *personal* meaning for you, that there is a *value* gained from stopping, and that you are *capable* of stopping. Once a smoker is even partially committed to quitting, he faces a dazzling array of methods ranging from the highly personal to the very commercial. Dozens of books and hundreds of magazine and newspaper articles champion any one of many methods. For starters, Jerome L. Schwartz, who conducted a survey of smoking control methods, listed everything from educational programs and chemotherapy to mail-order techniques and self-control.

•

The same surgeon general's report that stirred up the public in 1964 also stirred some interest among clinical psychologists to try aversion therapy on the now officially sanctioned problem. Whether it took publicity to start the bells ringing is not known, but it seems no mere coincidence that with few exceptions the research on aversion and smoking sprang up just a decade or so ago. The results as indicated in scientific journals are, to put it charitably, mixed. Once again there is little in the way of standardization of experiments or results, although lately the need for both has become more recognized.

Clinical experiments with smokers certainly have brought some novel additions to the aversion grab bag. One researcher teamed high-frequency noise to the act of smoking. Another triggered a .22-caliber rifle just 2 feet behind a smoker's head some 500 times. After exploding more rounds than in a victorious Banana Republic putsch, the researcher claimed success by reducing the smoker to 10 cigarettes a day from his normal 18. The question of hearing impairment was ignored.

One early and much imitated study was carried out by Gerrit Jan S. Wilde of the Wilhelmina Hospital in Amsterdam. Wilde was concerned that manipulating smokers to fear smoking could lead to undesirable side effects, such as increased anxiety. The psychologist instead devised a method that he believed would heighten a distaste for cigarettes without arousing anxiety and simultaneously provide smokers with a substitute.

Wilde came up with a Rube Goldberg device to blow hot, smoky air into the face of a subject while he puffed away. The client had to continue smoking until he could not tolerate the combination of machine smoke and his own, a period usually of about 10 to 15 seconds. Then the smoker extinguished his cigarette, muttered something like "I want to give up smoking," and received a reward of cool, mentholated air followed by a peppermint candy.

Wilde's original seven subjects repeated this pattern anywhere from 6 to 20 times in less than half an hour. Then, with the smoke machine off, each smoker lighted up so he could see that the cigarette itself had become sickening and offensive, not just the aversive setup. After two sessions, Wilde said, three pack-a-day smokers gave up the habit completely and two others cut back considerably. However, in a follow-up, the psychologist noted that all five "successes" later resumed their normal smoking patterns.

Wilde did notice something that seems to have escaped many researchers who followed. His method seemed to depend on the motivation of the smoker to get rid of his habit, and Wilde saw this as a major weakness since such motivation often appears low. "In many respects cigarette smoking resembles other compulsive behavior," Wilde noted. "There is, however, a very important difference in the fact that cigarette smoking is not socially undesirable." That observation was made a decade ago. A glance at most cocktail parties or public places will show that it still holds true.

A group of researchers at the New Jersey Neuro-Psychiatric Institute in Princeton refined Wilde's therapy. They devised a plywood box apparatus, about the size of an orange crate, which flashed the words "smoke" or "fresh air" according to what was hitting the smoker. Of 23 voluntary patients, only 9 completed the four-week session. They came in three times a week and went through the arduous routine, averaging 10 cigarettes a session. Six months later four of the people, who had smoked one to two packs a day, were not smoking at all and one was smoking less. However, the experimenters were not convinced their setup had done the job. Perhaps, they mused, the presession interview was, of itself, sufficient to develop an aversion or reinforce the client's desire to stop smoking. Or the orange crate might have turned the trick by itself, without any added smoking by the patients.

•

Early experiments bared two of the biggest problems in aversion or any other type of smoking therapy. First, there appears to be a very high remission rate, whether two months or six months or a year after treatment ends. Also there is a high dropout rate during the treatment itself. The smoker must be highly motivated before he tries and sticks with aversion therapy. This usually means he has tried to stop smoking before, and perhaps even succeeded for brief periods.

M. A. Hamilton Russell, a research worker at Maudsley Hospital in London, turned to another familiar method: electric shock. In a report in the *British Medical Journal,* Russell acknowledged the odds facing him. He said some 30 to 40 percent of men and women attending antismoking clinics manage to stop by the end of the clinical treatment, but a year later the rate of success drops to around 12 to 28 percent. The effect of the clinics is dubious, he concluded, since 20 to 30 percent of all smokers stop on their own. Because most people who consciously want to stop smoking cannot, Russell theorized that electrical aversion could work successfully through subconscious mechanisms.

Russell excluded 9 of 23 chest clinic patients who were not motivated sufficiently, because, he said, he was not in business to persuade "ambivalent" smokers to stop. Despite his resolve and selectivity, five of his clients dropped out of treatment, one because of severe depression. Several others became depressed and almost all were anxious, so Russell ended up administering antidepressants and other drugs to six of the smokers.

His shock box, a portable battery-driven type, administered "unpleasant but not intolerable" shocks which varied from subject to subject, depending on tolerance levels. (An experimenter must depend on the subject to tell him where to set the shock level. In other electrical aversive experiments, that level has been increased as the sessions progress and the person gets used to the shocks.) Russell's subjects sat with their backs to him with electrodes on their left forearms. They were told to start smoking in the usual way. During these trials they got shocked randomly when reaching for a pack, lighting up, or inhaling. The smokers also were told to imagine situations during a normal day in which smoking was most pleasurable, such as first thing in the morning or after a meal. When the subject had the scene in his mind, he told the therapist and received a shock on the same random schedule as the actual smoking trials, or about three out of four times. Unlike other experimenters, Russell continued the trials not only until all subjects stopped smoking (most stopped within five sessions), but also until the urge to smoke was minimal or completely absent. That ranged anywhere from 4 to 24 sessions. After one year, only six of the nine who completed treatment were still abstinent. Still Russell advocates electric shock for persistent smokers who have tried to stop in the past, and who have a strong motivation to break the habit.

•

Joseph R. Cautela, the Boston College professor who developed the "covert sensitization" method of aversion therapy, applied it to smokers. To repeat briefly, in covert sensitization the subject is told to imagine that he is about to engage in the particular behavior that is the target for modification. Then he is told to imagine a highly unpleasant reaction, usually nausea and vomiting. Theoretically this leads to avoidance of the actual behavior in a real-life situation.

As Cautela explained in an issue of *Psychological Reports*, he tells a subject that smoking is a habit which gives pleasure and reduces tension, that it is associated with many situations in life which tend to trigger the actual smoking, and that if the person can associate something unpleasant with smoking, his desire to smoke will be decreased or eliminated. Cautela tells the smoker to sit back in his chair, close his eyes, and try to relax. Then he instructs:

> I am going to ask you to imagine some scenes as vividly as you can. I don't want you to imagine that you are seeing yourself in these situations. I want you to imagine that you're actually *in* the situations. Do not only try to visualize the scenes but also try to feel, for example, the cigarette in your hand, or the back of the chair in which you are sitting. Try to use all your senses as though you are actually there. The scenes that I pick will be concerned with situations in which you are about to smoke. It is very important that you visualize the scenes as clearly as possible and try to actually feel what I describe to you even though it is unpleasant.

To say that the scenes are unpleasant is putting it mildly.
A typical scene for a college professor might go:

> You are sitting at your desk in the office preparing
> your lecture for class. There is a pack of cigarettes to
> your right. While you are writing, you put down your
> pencil and start to reach for a cigarette. As soon as
> you start reaching for the cigarette, you get a nau-
> seous feeling in your stomach. You begin to feel sick
> to your stomach, like you are about to vomit. You
> touch the package and bitter spit comes to your
> mouth. When you take the cigarette out of the pack,
> some pieces of food come into your throat. Now you
> feel sick and have stomach cramps.
>
> As you are about to put the cigarette in your mouth,
> you puke all over the cigarette, all over your hand
> and all over the package of cigarettes. The cigarette
> in your hand is very soggy and full of green vomit.
> There is a stink coming from the vomit. Snot is com-
> ing from your nose. Your hands feel all slimy and full
> of vomit. The whole desk is a mess. Your clothes are
> full of puke. You get up from your desk and turn
> away from the vomit and cigarettes. You immediately
> begin to feel better being away from the cigarettes.
> You go to the bathroom and wash up and feel great
> being away from the cigarettes.

Cautela then asks the smoker how intensely he felt the
nausea and disgust, and tells him to repeat the scene, visualizing every detail, smelling the vomit. He builds other, similar
scenes around situations in which the subject finds smoking
pleasurable, alternating them with "escape" scenes to reinforce the idea of not smoking. Cautela describes one of the
latter:

> You are at your desk working and you decide to
> smoke, and as soon as you decide to smoke you get

this funny sick feeling at the pit of your stomach. You
say to yourself, "The hell with it; I'm not going to
smoke!" As soon as you decide not to smoke you feel
fine and proud that you resisted temptation.

Cautela gives a smoker 10 aversive scenes and 10 escape
scenes at each therapy session, and instructs him to practice
all 20 scenes twice a day until the next session. He also tells
the smoker to say "Stop!" and imagine he is vomiting on a
cigarette if he is tempted to smoke. If the tension gets too great
in certain smoking situations, Cautela tells the subject to use
relaxation procedures, such as a couple of deep breaths. Cautela believes the procedure has merit and tells of cases in
which the nonsmoking behavior has lasted at least a year.

A group of experimenters at Sacramento State College in
California tried a method called "satiation" or "saturation"
therapy. Picture a cherry cheesecake freak who somehow,
maybe on a bet, manages to stuff down two entire cakes at one
sitting. He feels horrible for some time thereafter and never
wants to look a cherry cheesecake in the eye again. Or, as the
proverbial Jewish mother would say, "Too much of a good
thing. . . ." The Sacramento smokers constantly had to hold a
lighted cigarette and inhale at least every two to three minutes, either for 10 or 20 nearly consecutive hours. Within
about two hours of starting, the smokers showed the effects:
dizziness, shaking, sore throat, burning eyes, and nausea.
Four months later, 60 percent of the 20-hour group were nonsmokers; only 2 of 11 members of the 10-hour group could
make that boast.

Other kinds of satiation therapy also have been tried. A
smoking clinic at California State College at Los Angeles had
smokers puff rapidly to the ticking of a metronome. The clinic
also used the smoke-blowing box. One student involved in the
Cal State program launched his own, now-defunct, profit-
making smoke clinic. In addition to borrowing the college's
methods, the young entrepreneur added his own "saturation
therapy." He had his clients write "To hell with cigarettes"

1,000 times a day. If they followed his instructions religiously, perhaps they just would not have any time to smoke.

Other experimental procedures have combined more than one aversive method. A University of Notre Dame project had subjects use portable pocket-sized devices to shock themselves three times when they made a decision to smoke. If they still wanted the cigarette, they put foul-tasting quinine powder on their tongues just prior to lighting up. The same psychologist in charge of the experiment, Thomas L. Whitman, made up his own aversive pill for later projects. The pill created a burning sensation and a bitter taste about two minutes after being placed in the mouth. Little wonder since it contained, among other things, ginger, licorice, clove, and menthol. Based on follow-up studies to his tests, Whitman concluded that the pill had only a temporary effect on smoking behavior and that perhaps the motivation of all the volunteer subjects was the real key to any success.

A University of Oregon project combined three techniques. First, antismoking images were associated with specific, daily actions. (Getting up from a chair, for example, might lead to thoughts of a cancerous lung.) Next, the subject imagined himself in a smoking situation and then held his breath until that became "mildly painful," usually in 10 to 20 seconds. Finally, several subjects entered a small, closed room and while the therapist chattered on about the evils of smoking (burning eyes, hacking cough, shortness of breath, and so on), they actually experienced them as a thick, acrid cloud of smoke built up. But the experimenters concluded that using the three methods in combination was not too successful. After six months, only 20 percent of the group remained nonsmokers.

Still, the smoking researchers of the University of Oregon continue undaunted. "We try to create a warm, friendly relationship with each smoker and freely give appropriate verbal praise or punishment," says Edward Lichtenstein, director of the psychology clinic at the school. The punishment now consists of quick puffing to the beat of a metronome (about one drag every 6 seconds) as well as the old standby, a smoke-blowing box. In two studies all but one of 58 hard-core smokers stopped smoking by the end of treatment and 34 were still abstinent six months later. However, Lichtenstein is not sure what elements of the entire program were aiding success.

"When we provided the same kind of interpersonal relationship and praise without aversive conditioning, the participating smokers quit just as readily, but significantly more of them relapsed during the six month follow-up period," he says. In another Oregon study, smokers who were told not to get their hopes too high and who were not given a lot of verbal pats on the back made a considerably worse showing than the group undergoing the same trials in a highly supportive atmosphere.

Lichtenstein recounts a couple of nonlaboratory approaches to smoking cessation. The wife of one of the researchers (she liked to smoke while she was watching television) was permitted to smoke only while sitting in a certain chair in another room. Her smoking decreased and the chair was moved to the basement. Eventually she kicked the habit. A young psychologist who tried to get his fiancee to stop smoking did not fare as well. He was curt and almost unresponsive when she was smoking, but gave her a great deal of attention when she was not. His fiancee cut down on cigarettes until she became aware of what he was doing; then she started smoking more.

The Oregon psychologist is not very impressed with electrical aversion. "Unfortunately, a person readily discriminates between laboratory smoking, which is painful, and outside smoking, which is not," he says. Some researchers have tried to get around this by rigging up a special cigarette case that will give the smoker a shock anytime he opens it up. (This seems to require a lot more cooperation from the smoker than will probably be forthcoming over the long run.) Lichtenstein is sure of one thing: No matter what method is used, the important thing is for the smoker to be completely abstinent at the end of the experiment. The smokers who cut back to just a few a day invariably go back to their pretreatment level after a while, he says.

By conservative estimates, smokers who want to quit spend more than $50 million a year in the United States alone. Few of the methods used have shown consistently high rates of success when evaluated independently. But the demand is still there. So it really is no great surprise that attempts to cash in on the "new" method called "aversion therapy" popped up a couple of years ago all across the country. They range from one-office establishments such as Human Research Laboratories in New York City to the dozen or so Schick Centers for the Control of Smoking scattered throughout the West.

The Schick people—the same folks who are in the alcohol aversion business—used to call their operation "Schick Centers for the *Cure* of Smoking," but substituted the word "control" a couple of years back. The centers are clean and modern. They are smoothly and professionally run and they claim a phenomenally high success rate for the more than 20,000 smokers said to have gone through the clinics. A year after treatment, 68 percent of the former smokers are still abstinent, according to Alex Reuss, president of Schick Laboratories.

The Schick people started testing their smoking program in 1969 at their Seattle alcoholism treatment facility and opened the first separate center in 1971. All of Schick's therapists are nonprofessionals (and ex-smokers) who go through a two-week training program. "We don't need any medical experts or supervision," says Reuss, who successfully completed the program himself before it was introduced publicly. "We're not treating a malady or sickness as such. Smoking isn't an illness. If you'd put what we do in the hands of doctors, it would cost three times as much. We look at this as sort of like a health spa."

Schick spends a lot of money on media advertising and promotional literature. "Our research shows that you have to 'grab' a smoker five times before he calls or comes in," Reuss says. "So it takes a lot of effort on their part, but it means they'll be committed. It just doesn't work if a person is dragged in or if he's just doing it to ease his conscience."

Schick newspaper advertisements are filled with copy

and diagrams offering the Schick view of "social addictions" like smoking. "Addiction comes without warning through the *Instinctive Memory* which is much more sensitive than the *Reasoning Mind*," the ads claim. "At the Schick Center you can build up in your *Instinctive Memory* negative associations with smoking. Now your emotions start motivating you not to smoke."

There is also a rather faddish and not particularly apt comparison between smoking and playing tennis. "The weight of the tennis racket against the ball has an effect on the muscles which causes strong impressions to be made on the Instinctive Memory. These impressions cannot be changed by conversation alone. To improve your tennis game you must use the racket and the ball under expert guidance. The coach must correct your faults at the exact moment to improve your game. A reprimand at the club house later will not have any effect on the Instinctive Memory."

The ads make no guarantee of success beyond this statement: "Aversion conditioning, or negative associations made simultaneously with the act of taking a drug, is effective." Neither do the ads mention the price of treatment, which is now up to a hefty $450. Reuss says, with some justification, that an absolute moneyback guarantee would be a disservice to the client, so Schick has not offered one. Just having nearly $500 invested can be a powerful motivation for success.

When the smoker finally decides to try the Schick program, he fills out a four-page questionnaire that elicits information that will be helpful to the therapist later in informal chats with the client. It asks what the smoker expects to gain by quitting, why he smokes, in what settings he smokes the most, and how important he feels it is to stop now. Some medical data are also given; Schick says it will not accept people with heart problems.

For five days before the first session, the smokers wear golf-stroke counters on their wrists to keep track of how much they actually smoke, a figure that often comes as a shock. Starting on Monday morning, and for an hour a day for the rest of the week, the client receives his aversive conditioning.

The therapy room at the Schick center is tiny. In one corner there is a wooden table covered with hundreds of smelly cigarette butts and ashes. Above it, a mirror is mounted on the wall and all around are colorful cigarette ads clipped from magazines. A young housewife, her long black hair tied in a knot, is gazing intently into the mirror, puffing on a cigarette every six seconds or so at the direction of the therapist. The therapist, another young woman, is seated about 6 feet away and to the rear of the smoker. Her mouth and nose are covered with a white gauze mask. She is administering frequent shocks to the smoker and telling her to continue puffing. The room smells from stale cigarettes. The constant tapping on the shock machine sounds like Morse code. The housewife is coughing, her eyes red and teary, her clothes and hair reeking of smoke.

"Okay, let's take a coffee break," the therapist says. "How do you feel?"

The housewife walks over to the therapist's table. She looks emotionally drained, but manages a smile. "Fine, fine. I feel great."

"Do you think you still have that desire to smoke?"

"Oh, God, no. I can't see how I ever . . . oh, it's just awful. And it all smells so much."

The two women chat for the next 10 minutes or so. This too is part of the therapy, a reward for not smoking, some personal interaction and support. It also helps keep the negative associations directed toward smoking and not to the therapist or the whole clinical setup, Schick officials say. The women discuss what problems the smoker is having at home (she has not told her husband and is trying to surprise him with her success) and how to deal with some of the temptations to smoke. Then it is time for another 15 minutes of random shock.

In addition to the shocks, smokers at Schick centers take part in saturation therapy. Four or five smokers go into an airtight room and sit around a large metal wash basin filled with hundreds of cigarette butts. They all light up and quickly puff away on enough cigarettes to shroud the room in an acrid haze, thick enough to obscure each from the person sitting next to him. Coughing and teary eyed, the smokers are led out of the room and into fresh air. The same "quick-puff" therapy also is used in individual treatment rooms.

An important part of the Schick program is a follow-up set of eight weekly group meetings after the week of aversion therapy. At these sessions, problems are discussed, films are shown, and nutritional advice is given. (The successful Schick graduate normally puts on about 4 pounds in the weeks following the final cigarette.) Although Schick does not offer refunds, it promises to "recycle" any client who falls off the wagon within a year from the start of his original treatment.

A. Brent Garber, director of the comparatively small Human Research Laboratories in New York, says his organization's follow-up group sessions are an integral part of therapy. "Out of the people who have failed, I'm sure not one went to all the group meetings," he says. Human Research claims that a representative sampling of 100 out of the first 400 patients to undergo the program shows that 71 percent are still nonsmokers at anywhere from two months to a year later. Although Human Research employs a smoke-blowing machine, quick-puff therapy, and 20 to 40 shocks in a three-minute period while the smoker is puffing feverishly, Garber says the aversive techniques are just one part of the entire treatment.

"Aversion can be very useful to get someone off smoking for the short term," he says. "Then we can work with them to build up their own confidence. Problem smokers really begin to feel there's nothing they can do to stop smoking. Aversive conditioning is sort of like a coach's pre-game pep talk. We boost their spirits temporarily and that helps them initiate a permanent attitude change."

•

Even if the claims of success are completely accurate, the aversion smoking clinics are anything but an exact science. It is impossible to say if a "cured" individual will start smoking again. Also, there really is not any way to predict who will benefit from such an experience, though it appears it would probably be a waste of time and money if the smoker is not completely committed to giving up the habit.

A case in point: Two Los Angeles orchestra leaders and friends, Gary Michaels, 42, and Lew Malin, 37, went through Schick together about three years ago. Michaels has not smoked since the end of treatment; Malin resumed about six weeks later.

"I had been smoking since I was 18 and was up to two-and-a-half to three packs a day," Michaels recounts. "I'm also a singer and, boy, it was really getting to me. I tried to knock it cold turkey and then by tapering off. Maybe I'd stop for a week or even a couple of months, but I still had that great need and I was going through terrible periods of suffering. It got to the point where I would do anything to stop.

"I saw the Schick ads, went, and stopped smoking the first day. Even more important, I didn't have that desire to smoke anymore. I can't pinpoint what did it, whether it was the shock or what. And it's not really a frightening experience. They just made you constantly aware of the smell and the feeling."

Malin was also a fairly heavy smoker and his wife was putting some pressure on him to stop, so he tried Schick. "I feel that they do a good job," he says. "They present a case against smoking and put you through a hell of an ordeal. And I made a sincere attempt to do what they said; I really expected something to happen. It did work too—for about six weeks."

In retrospect Malin says his smoking habit is probably ingrained a lot deeper than he had thought. Even though he went to Schick with a "spirit of cooperation" and was impressed with the lab's array of techniques, Malin says he probably did not want to stop smoking badly enough. "I only went to one of those follow-up sessions, although I probably should have gone to more," he says. Looking back on the experience a year later, Malin realizes that his own reaction was rather unemotional. "I took it all in and said, 'Yes, that's right,' but there was something lacking in intensity. And I guess the only reason I stopped altogether for a while was because I had too much pride and didn't want to look bad."

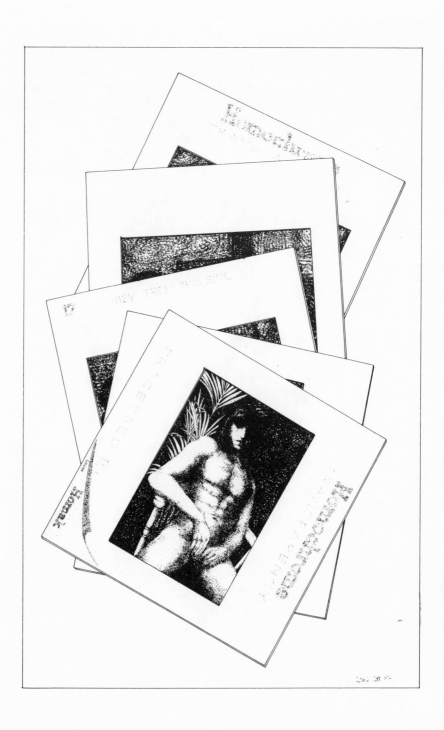

Chapter IV

THE GAYEST SLIDE
SHOW ON EARTH

The slide flashes on the screen and Martin studies it intently. "Just my type," he chuckles to himself, wondering at the same time whether he would have had the nerve to approach such a good-looking boy if he had seen him in a bar the week before. The slide leaves nothing to the imagination —the boy is definitely "hung"—but even more enticing to Martin is the slim build and classic Joe College face, right down to the shock of corn-silk hair sweeping across the forehead. Martin shifts uneasily in the wooden armchair, careful not to remove his head from the elongated viewing box. Foam earmuffs almost completely isolate him from the outside world. It is just him and Fraternity Fred, and right now Fred is draped seductively on an orange bedspread that accentuates his nudity, his supple limbs, his. . . .

That is when the jolt hits. It is on the right leg this time and it feels like he is being jabbed by an ice pick. Martin's reveries are shattered. He looks at Fred for just another instant before punching the button to his right, thus ending the electric shock and removing the slide from the screen. Instantly a *Playboy* centerfold pops onto the screen and Martin glances at the leggy brunette with some detachment and also some relief since he knows he will not be shocked as long as he remains face to face with Miss July.

The use of aversion therapy to try to change homosexuals into heterosexuals has a relatively brief history, but there are indications that in the last 10 years or so thousands of male homosexuals and some females have undergone aversive treatment in an attempt to change with whom they go to bed. A recent poll of behavior therapists showed that 45 percent of those who responded favored aversion therapy as the preferred method of redirecting homosexuals toward heterosexuality, far surpassing any other method. The growth in the use of aversion has coincided with the birth and meteoric rise of the gay liberation movement and the two have collided head-on in a battle that goes to the very roots of just what homosexuality is and whether a "cure" is either necessary or desirable.

Martin decided it was, or at least that he would try for Monica's sake. The 22-year-old British librarian met Monica, two years his senior, some five months before treatment and they immediately took a liking to each other. Martin found himself becoming emotionally attached to Monica although he lacked any sexual desire for her. Finally he decided to break off the relationship, explaining his past to Monica, but she persuaded him to seek professional treatment.

Like the vast majority of homosexuals, there is nothing unusual in Martin's appearance or manner to tip off anyone that he happens to like to go to bed with other men. He carries his 6-foot frame with the grace of all natural athletes, his voice is deep, and his blue eyes direct. The eldest of two boys in a closely knit Methodist family, he had a "normal" childhood. Martin learned about sex from classmates when he was 14 and he began the kind of fooling around with a school friend not untypical of boys that age. At 16 he became aware that he was sexually attracted to other males and occasionally hung around men's rooms without incident. Two years later Martin had his first real homosexual contact; he was picked up in a bar by an older man. Over the next few years he had a couple of short "affairs" with other men, and at times made pickups in gay bars and public lavatories. Before he met Monica, he had been out with several other girls but had not been very interested in them.

When Martin showed up at Crumpsall Hospital in Manchester saying he wanted to be "normal and have children," he could not have known that his case would be the first in what has become a classic study of the use of aversion therapy on homosexuals. Conducted by a British team composed of psychiatrist M. J. MacCulloch and psychologist M. P. Feldman, the study focused on their treatment of 43 homosexuals (described in clinical detail in a 1971 monograph, *Homosexual Behaviour: Therapy and Assessment*). It is the most thorough and apparently the most successful large-scale project undertaken in the field. The study has been criticized by other psychologists on methodological grounds, but it seems hard to argue with the figures MacCulloch and Feldman present. Out of 43 patients (7 of whom never completed treatment), 25 were "improved" in a follow-up averaging 20 months after treatment: of these, 13 were engaging in heterosexual intercourse, 7 were otherwise actively heterosexual, and the remaining 5 showed signs of being inclined along these lines. (At least 2 of the 25 later returned to homosexual practices.) The 58 percent success rate reported by MacCulloch and Feldman is probably more responsible than anything else for the increased use of aversion therapy with homosexuals in the last few years.

•

Louis W. Max is credited with the first use of modern aversive techniques on a homosexual in the mid-1930s. Upon fantasizing homosexual behavior, Max's patient was immediately given high-intensity electric shocks. Max said that the emotional value of the sexual stimulus was reduced, and four months after treatment the patient had a "95 percent rate of success." Unfortunately, Max did not explain what that meant and the report was virtually ignored. Instead, homosexuals continued to be treated by traditional psychotherapy, including analysis, despite a lack of hard evidence that long and costly psychiatric sessions turned homosexuals into card-carrying heterosexuals. Indeed, the evidence is to the contrary. The British Wolfenden Report in 1957, which led to the legalization of private homosexual acts between consenting adults, said medical experts were not able to document even one case of the complete conversion of an adult from exclusive homosexuality to satisfactory heterosexuality. However, the most extensive and optimistic study, reported in 1962 by the Society of Medical Psychoanalysts in New York, claimed that out of 106 male homosexuals who underwent private treatment, 27 percent were exclusively heterosexual when they last reported to their analysts and another 12 percent showed some degree of "improvement." The report covered a nine-year period, and at the time information was gathered, about one third of the patients still were undergoing treatment after more than 350 sessions of analysis. Without a follow-up, the report is perhaps interesting, but hardly persuasive.

Dr. Kurt Freund, a Czechoslovakian psychiatrist, picked up the trail of aversion therapy some 20 years after Louis Max's report. Using a mixture of caffein and apomorphine to produce nausea and vomiting, he showed his patients alternate slides of dressed and naked men. In a second phase of treatment, he gave all his subjects the male sex hormone, testosterone, and after seven hours showed them heterosexual stag films in an attempt to increase their approaches to women. Out of 67 patients followed up five to eight years after treatment, 22 had established some heterosexual behavior, but only 12 had maintained such behavior, and only 3 had broken off all homosexual activity following the sessions.

A 40-year-old homosexual in Bristol, England, underwent a harsh form of chemical aversion under the guidance of Basil James of Glenside Hospital, Stapleton. The man's retail business was on the verge of bankruptcy because he had been spending well beyond his means—the only way he felt he could attract desirable young men. Treatment was carried out in a small, almost pitch-black room. The patient was not permitted food or drink. Every two hours he was given an injection of apomorphine followed by two ounces of brandy. James explained that drinking was associated with the man's pattern of homosexual behavior and, besides, the brandy accentuated the nausea-producing quality of the apomorphine. As soon as the patient became nauseous, a bright light suddenly illuminated a piece of cardboard containing photos of nude or almost nude men. The patient then was asked to fantasize experiences that he had had with his current male lover. Subsequently a tape was played in which James "explained" the causes of the man's homosexuality and its adverse affect on his life. The tape ended in histrionics, with James scolding the man for his "sickening," "nauseating," and otherwise unacceptable behavior. The final moment was the sound of someone vomiting—which usually made the patient feel wretched enough to vomit too.

This treatment was repeated every 2 hours, without a break for rest or nourishment, for 30 hours. After a day's rest, the treatment was repeated, this time for 32 hours. The next night the patient was awakened every 2 hours to listen to a rather congratulatory tape detailing what would be accomplished if his homosexuality was changed. For the next three days, he was given injections of testosterone and told to go to his room if he felt any sexual excitement. There he would find "carefully selected photographs of sexually attractive women" and recordings by a female singer "whose performance is generally recognized as 'sexy.' " Some 18 months after treatment James said his patient had a new mood of confidence and had no recurrence of his homosexual drives. He found a girl friend and had sexual relations with her which he described as giving him considerable physical satisfaction "though not having the same emotional component as his homosexual experiences."

Some chemical aversion therapy is still being used with homosexuals today but most therapists prefer other methods, mainly for reasons of better control and measurement. Another, less-discussed factor may be that the death of at least one homosexual patient was tied directly to such therapy. Without mentioning the name of the therapist involved, Britain's *Medico Legal Journal* reported the case of W. T., a 34-year-old hotel manager who had tried psychotherapy, tranquilizing drugs, and even electroconvulsive treatment before turning to aversion therapy. W. T. was chronically tense, fearful of discovery, and subject to attacks of panic, sweating, and palpitations of the heart.

The man's therapist used a medicine shelf of drugs. Apomorphine, emetine, and tincture of ipecacuanha were used to produce nausea; lysergic acid, or LSD, was used to induce hallucinations while the therapist suggested heterosexual fantasies. The main ingredient of ipecacuanha is emetine, used mainly to treat amoebic dysentery. Some people are unpredictably sensitive to emetine, which has been proven toxic to the heart, and death has occurred after two 1-grain injections. W. T. took 19¹/₂ grains of emetine in six days. Within a week he was dead from emetine poisoning.

•

Although most early aversive techniques were aimed at reducing the homosexual drive through direct punishment, MacCulloch and Feldman dived back into the pool of animal experiments and surfaced with something they call "anticipatory avoidance." They said homosexual behavior is really a chain of events beginning with the overt act of looking at an attractive male, so that act of looking must be dealt with first. Rather than suppress the looking directly through shock, they opted for a technique in which the patient actively avoided the previously attractive stimulus—other men—by avoiding or escaping from a punishing electric shock. The therapists decided that their new technique could lead to a new response, one acquired quickly and highly resistant to being extinguished. This would provide time for the patient to acquire or reacquire an interest in heterosexual behavior.

The researchers' much copied technique seems simple, perhaps even simplistic. (In a subsequent critique, psychologists Stanley Rachman and John Teasdale noted: ". . . the surprising thing about aversion therapy is *not* that its effects are uncertain, but rather that it works at all.") Patients set up a hierarchy of about eight photos of attractive males from least to most attractive with photos of females, the most attractive first, alternating after each male photo. The idea is to condition an initial avoidance response more easily by making the first male photo only mildly attractive but following it immediately by the most attractive female slide.

MacCulloch and Feldman's first group of patients consisted of 41 male homosexuals and two 18-year-old lesbian lovers. Treatment ranged from 5 sessions to 38, the average being 20. One of the most valuable parts of the study was a detailed breakdown giving an almost too intimate dossier on the patients, including age of initial masturbation and current masturbatory fantasy; favorite homosexual practice; age of preferred partner; and, possibly most important, whether there had ever been any heterosexual behavior, and if so, what kind it was and when it developed. The men and women also were rated on a scale of 1 to 6 developed by American zoologist-turned-sex guru, Alfred Kinsey. A rating of 1 indicated total heterosexual behavior and 6, complete homosexual behavior. Twelve of the subjects were rated 5 and 19 subjects were rated 6; none were 1 or 2. Other characteristics of the group included a better education than the population at large, little family history of psychiatric illness (although 25 were judged to have a "personality disorder"), and a current marriage for 7 subjects. Most were in the 26- to 30-year-old bracket although 13 subjects were under 25 and 9 were over 40. Perhaps significantly, nearly half (18) were forced to sign up for the therapy as a result of court order-related actions.

For treatment the patients sat in a wooden chair in a dark room, 6 feet in front of a 2- by 3-foot screen. Enclosing the screen was a tapered box that narrowed as it approached the patient and which had a cutout for his neck. Homemade earmuffs further limited any possible outside interference. Electrodes were attached to each leg and shocks were administered randomly to one leg or the other. The instructions were simple. A male patient was told he would see a male photo and that several seconds later he *might* receive a shock. He was to watch the slide for as long as he found it sexually attractive, but could turn it off whenever he wanted by pressing a switch. This also turned off the unpleasant shock. There were no shocks when the screen was blank.

The first male slide then clicked on. If the patient switched it off within eight seconds he was not shocked. This was called an "avoidance response." If he did not switch off the slide within eight seconds, he was shocked until he did so. This was called an "escape response." At the same time he turned off a slide, the patient was also told to say no in hopes of further strengthening his avoidance of homosexual activities. After a time even a person who gets a kick out of being shocked (and there have been some cases of masochists actually enjoying similar treatment) is going to catch on or tire of the routine. So after the patient avoided the shock three times in a row, the routine varied. One third of the time he would be able to switch off the slide immediately and avoid the shock; another third he had to wait the eight seconds and get a brief shock; and the final third he was allowed to eject the slide and avoid the shock after a brief delay. When the patient consistently tried to switch off the slide after one or two seconds and reported that he was indifferent to or even disliked the photo, the next male slide flashed on and the process started all over again.

Amost every time a male slide went off, a female slide filled the screen. "The fact that the female slide is associated with the cessation of pain increases the likelihood that it will acquire positive reinforcing qualities," the researchers said. They believe that many homosexuals are not merely indifferent to females, but often fear heterosexual contact. Thus the researchers' formula was male = pain + anxiety, female = relief. The patient could ask that the female slide be returned to the screen but it could be removed only by a therapist, "so that his [the patient's] habit of avoiding females was not strengthened in the training situation." An interesting supposition, but perhaps a bit farfetched in reality.

Among the 25 of 43 original patients considered improved at follow-ups ranging from one to three years was Martin the librarian. He took part in 28 sessions over a two-week period as an inpatient at Crumpsall Hospital. As treatment progressed he reported a steady decrease in the attractiveness of male photos and a corresponding increase in the allure of female slides. After the two weeks, he and Monica went on a vacation and had mutually satisfactory intercourse with Martin having "some slight remaining, although easily controlled, interest in men." The lovebirds got married the following year. "I can now look forward to living normally and having a home life and children—a year ago this seemed less and less likely," Martin told the therapists. "I feel that progress is being more than maintained."

MacCulloch and Feldman next decided to do a three-part comparative study using an even more elaborate form of "anticipatory avoidance," classical conditioning in which a male photo always produced a shock, and individual psychotherapy in which the patient discussed his problems with a psychiatrist. A total of 30 patients were randomly assigned to the three groups. As expected, only two of the psychotherapy patients improved (they only had 12 one-hour sessions) and both relapsed. The results of the other two groups are a bit confusing since most, after one treatment, were given the other therapy. But MacCulloch and Feldman concluded that *despite* their expectations, there was little difference in the success rate between the two different aversion therapies. They claimed a "probable" total success rate of around 60 percent. Undaunted, they continue to believe their original method is superior. It provides a constant flow of information on how the patient is reacting and thus what steps the therapist should be taking, they say. Also it is easier to manipulate anxiety, speeding up avoidance learning and making it less susceptible to wearing out, they add. In short the therapists say anticipatory avoidance is "likely to increase the *efficiency* if not the *efficacy* of treatment."

MacCulloch and Feldman also claim that through psychological testing they can predict the outcome of treatment for future patients. To prove their point, however, they engage in some Monday morning quarterbacking, working backward with their final results to "predict" what kind of patient would have succeeded. The major prognostic sign, they say, is prior pleasurable heterosexual experience. Another is the absence of a personality disorder of what they call the weak-willed or attention-seeking type. Finally, there is the pretreatment score a patient receives on a sexual orientation method questionnaire devised to measure homo- and hetero-erotic orientation. Using this "triple sieve" to select certain patients and turn down others "would vastly increase the effective use of therapist time," MacCulloch and Feldman say. However, even they are a little disturbed by one "puzzling exception" who would have been excluded from treatment based on the triple sieve, but who nonetheless was successful in making a

heterosexual adjustment. How many therapists would be willing to exclude a patient from therapy because he may not
succeed? Still, MacCulloch and Feldman insist, "It seems
mandatory, both on economic and on ethical grounds, to use a
treatment which will enable the greatest number of patients to
be treated successfully in any given unit of time." They go on
to suggest that the therapy be as automated as possible so that
it would require "little more than general supervision by a
junior psychologist or even by a suitably trained nurse."

In their critique, Rachman and Teasdale raise a question
basic to all aversion therapy. Do patients really bridge the
seemingly enormous gap between pressing buttons and getting shocked in a clinic and making the "appropriate" responses in real-life situations, and if so, how? "Patients know
perfectly well that when they leave the clinic and approach
the abnormal sexual object or indulge in the deviant sexual
behavior, they will no longer receive electric shocks," Rachman and Teasdale say. "Nevertheless, a high proportion of the
patients did 'make the generalization' from the highly artifi-
cial clinical situation to the outside world." MacCulloch and
Feldman have a two-pronged explanation. Treatment is effective, they believe, because there is both an uncontrolled reflex
action (turning away from an attractive male because anxiety
has started to build up) and a well-thought-out response.
"Patients made it clear that they reflected both upon their
experiences in treatment and their changes in response outside treatment," they say.

•

The MacCulloch-Feldman technique has been adopted
and adapted widely, particularly in clinics and hospitals connected with universities in the United States. The department
of child psychiatry at the University of Missouri has used an
automated version of the therapy on children, one of the
youngest described as a 15-year-old male prostitute who was
in a correctional institution. In some cases the therapist was a
first-year graduate student without any special skills in the
area but with "a high degree of interest." The counseling

center at the University of Oregon has used anticipatory avoidance with monthly booster sessions up to a year after initial treatment.

As part of the requirement for his Ph.D. in clinical psychology at the University of North Carolina, Barry A. Tanner used a modified MacCulloch-Feldman approach on 26 male homosexuals. Tanner originally intended to do his work at the state-run Atlanta Regional Mental Hospital where he was working, but the Georgia director of mental health turned down the proposal because it involved a "socially explosive type of subject matter." Undeterred, Tanner plowed ahead with the project at a private Atlanta clinic, the Center for Behavior Change. The psychologist's preliminary reports do not provide enough of a follow-up period to determine the success of the total program; but there are interesting facets to his work.

In one of the few attempts to resolve the question of just how intense an electric shock is required in aversion therapy, Tanner randomly assigned his patients to two groups. One always received 5 milliampere shocks, a healthy jolt. Members of the other group picked their own level, the maximum they said they could tolerate; all but one of the group selected less than 5 milliamperes. The program consisted of 20 sessions of 45 minutes each using a commercially available shock-slide machine. The primary measure of success or failure was a change in penile circumference measured by a device called a "plethysmograph." The patients also rated their fear of electric shock by circling a number from 1 to 10 along a horizontal line. Six men dropped out before the first session and eight more did not complete all 20 sessions. Tanner found that the higher a man's fear rating, the fewer the number of sessions he was likely to attend and the lower the level of current he picked for himself—results that plain common sense would lead you to expect. He also found that the number of sessions attended by the men receiving 5 milliamperes of shock did not differ significantly from the variable-shock group. However, the 5-milliampere group showed a greater change in the heterosexual direction after the last session. Tanner cited reports that a minimum of 20 milliamperes is required over a long period before painful muscular contraction occurs, but he selected 5 milliamperes for a simple and very sound reason: He personally could tolerate little more than that level of shock.

•

Dr. Nathaniel McConaghy, a young Australian psychiatrist who teaches at the University of New South Wales in Sydney, has been active in the homosexual aversion field for several years. In his initial work with 40 male homosexuals, he compared drug aversion therapy with a type of aversion-relief treatment, measuring penis volume change as one indicator of success. In the first procedure patients were injected with 1.5 milligrams of apomorphine prior to the projection of a nude male slide. If this was not sufficient to produce 10 minutes of severe nausea, the dose was increased up to a hefty 6 milligrams. The patient was asked to become as sexually aroused as possible and then to turn on the projector about a minute before nausea set in.

In the second method the patient was shown 14 slides of words and phrases of various aspects of homosexuality that he found stimulating. He read each one aloud every 10 seconds, and immediately received an electric shock painful enough to make him flinch. After the 14 slides and shocks, a slide related to heterosexuality clicked on and stayed on for 40 seconds without any shocks—the "relief." Dr. McConaghy used both shock and drug methods for five days straight. He reported that significantly more patients said they resumed homosexual relations after the shock treatment. But although there were "significant changes" toward heterosexuality for the entire group, nine of the men became more firmly homosexual, something the psychiatrist could not explain. A year later about half the patients reported reduced homosexual feelings and half, not necessarily the same patients, said they had increased heterosexual feelings, including intercourse for many. All the patients, however, still were aware of some homosexual feelings. Also, the period of a year wiped out any differences in the outcome of the two different techniques. Dr. McConaghy argues that any heterosexual increase was not a result of the aversion therapy itself, but rather due to patients' greater awareness of their existing but latent heterosexual feelings once their homosexual feelings were reduced.

•

Another major area of aversive therapy used with homosexuals is "covert sensitization," in which the undesired behavior and the punishment are paired in the imagination. While treating a homosexual patient a dozen years ago, psychologist M. M. Miller reckoned that most homosexuals had experienced disgust at one time or another while having sexual relations with another man. Miller hypnotized his patient to bring into clear focus the revulsion he once felt when performing fellatio on an uncircumcised male. The psychologist closely and repeatedly associated this with visualized current homosexual practices. After several sessions, Miller says, the man became nauseated by his present lover and broke off all homosexual contacts.

Therapists S. Gold and I. Neufeld reported success in treating a 16-year-old boy convicted of soliciting men in lavatories of a railway station. First, they lessened the youth's anxiety. Then, while relaxed, he was encouraged to visualize a repulsive old geezer. When the youth had such a character in mind, the geezer was changed into increasingly more attractive images, but always surrounded by some danger such as a policeman lurking nearby. Then the boy was presented with scenes of an attractive young man and woman. The woman was associated with pleasant suggestions; the man with unpleasant imagery. After 10 sessions, the youth said he was able to avoid homosexual contacts in fantasy and reality, although he still felt some attraction to young men.

Two Scottish therapists used anxiety provoking scenes on a 31-year-old married homosexual with two children. In one scene the man imagines himself in a lavatory, approached by an ugly, knife-wielding man who threatens to "slice your balls off" unless the patient complies with the man's homosexual demands. The patient escapes, drives home, and is immensely relieved. In another scene he is about to have sex with an attractive man in his car when he sees his wife's face in the window and is panic stricken. He drives home, finds his wife has been there all the time, and is relieved again. The patient was told to visualize the scenes on his own whenever he felt a homosexual urge. Several months later he reported no homosexual fantasy or activity.

On the other hand, Barry M. Maletzky, of the Department of Neuropsychiatry, U.S. Army Lyster Hospital at Fort Rucker, Alabama, claims that covert sensitization by itself was ineffective with a number of patients who found it "not strong enough" or had trouble visualizing the noxious scenes. So he beefed up the covert process with 10 male homosexuals and bisexuals by having them sniff valeric acid, which has a powerful noxious odor, at the point when the unpleasant elements were introduced in the imagined scene. The scenes were constructed with the help of the patient and used what each one found most enjoyable, and most disgusting, about his homosexual behavior. The smell of the acid remained in the room until the client "escaped" from the imaginary homosexual scene. Those scenes were not exactly fairy tales. One example:

> You're at the beach with a special person, John. Imagine the ocean, the smell of salt air. You lie down behind a sand dune and start to embrace and undress each other. You can see his penis hard and stiff. He starts rubbing it back and forth. But as you get closer you notice a strange odor and you see small white worms, like lice, crawling in the hair around his penis! You're touching them with your mouth! It's disgusting and it's making you sick. Some of them have gotten onto you. They're crawling into your mouth. Your stomach starts to churn and food particles catch in your throat. Big chunks of vomit come into your mouth. Vomit dribbles down your chin. You can see the worms still, crawling in your puke, and you get sicker than before. You grab your trunks, clean yourself off, and run away as quickly as you can. As you do, you feel better, your stomach begins to settle down and you can breathe deeply the fresh air of the ocean. You notice the bright blue sky, the fresh smell of the ocean and feel much calmer and relaxed.

Three to five different scenes were presented twice per session for five sessions. In between, the men listened to recordings of the scenes twice a week while sniffing the acid. They were also told to seek out homosexual friends and haunts purposely and then sniff a vial of the acid. Several ways of measuring the client's reaction were used, including a "temptation test" that resembles the kind of soliciting and entrapment for which certain police forces are notorious. Both at the end of treatment and a year later, each man was approached by a "solicitor" employed by Maletzky but unknown to the client. If the solicitation was turned down, the patient passed; if there was even a tentative response, he failed. One patient failed both tests, another only the year-end test (after which he had 10 "booster" sessions). "Although ethical objections can be raised," Maletzky acknowledges, "objective assessment was necessary and we are unaware of any studies to indicate that widely spaced and unfulfilled 'solicitations' would alter treatment or add damage to a maladaptive life-style." He seems to be saying that since homosexuals are already sick, you cannot make them much sicker.

Allen E. Shealey has used something he calls a "cognitive-behavioral" approach with homosexuals. In one case he used covert sensitization by pairing homosexual fantasies with an image of the patient's mother mutilated in a gory accident. In addition, the client was told to refrain from urinating for as long as possible, and when he finally relieved himself he was to say over and over, "Women find me very attractive." He also was told to stop masturbating to male images and photos and instead start using female scenes and pictures. Finally, the man was told that each time he had an erotic image when meeting males on the street, he was to picture the man wearing a dress and having long hair and breasts. This was supposed to make the female image more positive by coupling it with sexual arousal, although it was undertaken "at the risk of having him become attracted to transvestites," Shealy says. The client reported overt homosexual behavior was eliminated.

Other treatments reported include: "olfactory aversion" in which the patient narrates a recent pleasurable encounter with another male and simultaneously sniffs ammonium sulfide (odor of rotten eggs), butyric acid (dirty underwear smell), and aromatic ammonia (smelling salts); deprivation of fluids followed by potent diuretics just prior to treatment with the promised reward of a sip of a cold drink if the patient's penis responds to female slides; and "fading in" over the slide of an attractive naked man a second slide showing nauseating running sores.

•

Considering that nearly half of all behavior therapists responding to a recent survey favored aversion therapy as their chief method for redirecting homosexuals, and given the controversial aspects of the therapy itself along with the inflammatory nature of recent debates over homosexuality, it is no wonder that this area has been one of the most hotly disputed in the entire field of behavior modification. For example, a gay activist group at the University of Minnesota, Minneapolis, has accused the medical school there of a "form of psychological castration" because it uses electrical aversion therapy for homosexuals. There have been frequent confrontations at professional meetings. A gay liberation group "invaded" a national convention of the American Psychiatric Association and interrupted the Australian psychiatrist, Dr. Nathaniel McConaghy, when he tried to deliver a paper on his use of aversion therapy. Dr. McConaghy started reading, but was almost immediately halted with shouts of, "Vicious!" "Torture!" and "Get your rocks off that way?"

"If you'll just listen, I'm sure you'll find I'm on your side," Dr. McConaghy told the hecklers. "I've gone on television urging an end to discrimination against homosexuals." Dr. McConaghy managed to complete his reading, but the rest of the session ended up in a shambles.

At a convention of the Western Psychological Association, a booth set up by Farrall Instrument Company (a large supplier of equipment for aversion therapy including the "visually keyed shocker" for homosexuals) was the target of a protest by a gay group. "We have come here today to protest your inhuman device and to ask you to voluntarily leave this place," announced Morris Kight, a Los Angeles gay leader. "We accuse you of genocide against the gay community." Overstated, of course, but the accusation clearly shows the hatred of gay militants for aversion therapy. The *Advocate*, a nationwide gay newspaper, reported that after the demonstration, the Farrall booth was "suddenly deluged by male psychologists placing orders for the machines and requesting more information, although several other psychologists told the gays that they would not use such a device."

The survey of behavior therapists referred to previously was carried out by Gerald C. Davison of State University of New York at Stony Brook and G. Terence Wilson of Rutgers University. For those who did not list aversion therapy as a first choice, 38 percent listed it as runner-up. The respondents claimed a suspiciously high success rate of 60 percent in decreasing homosexual behavior in their clients, and estimated that 46 percent showed a significant increase in heterosexual behavior. Nearly 9 out of 10 of the therapists denied that homosexuality is, by itself, evidence of psychopathology, and said they believed it is possible for a homosexual to be happy and well adjusted. Yet in related tests to determine attitudes, the therapists in all cases rated homosexuality "worse off" than heterosexuality, saying it was less good, more tense, less dominant, less masculine, less rational, and more passive. And although 87 percent of those answering said they would treat a homosexual to make him or her more at ease with being gay, some 13 percent said they had treated or would consider treating homosexuals against their will in an attempt to make them heterosexual.

Neither of the surveyors, who are behavior therapists themselves, are fans of aversion therapy for homosexuals. "Attempts have usually been made to change homosexual orientations with undue and probably unjustifiable reliance on aversion therapy," they say. The complexities of the issues involved, such as the differences between male and female homosexuals, have been too often overlooked, they add. "Indeed, behavior therapists have aimed primarily at reducing or eliminating homosexual behavior via aversive procedures, and only secondarily, in some cases, at directly fostering heterosexual behavior as an alternative mode of sexual expression." It would be much more effective, they suggest, to reinforce heterosexual behavior than to punish homosexual behavior, if that is what the client truly wants.

There can be little disagreement that the choice of behavioral goals, the final outcome of any treatment, should be the client's. Yet for years, traditional psychiatry diagnosed homosexuality as a sickness. That all changed in December 1973 when the American Psychiatric Association, under tremendous internal and external pressure, eliminated homosexuality as a category of "mental disorder." Instead, homosexuality was categorized as a "sexual orientation disturbance" to refer to "individuals whose sexual interests are directed primarily toward people of the same sex and who are either disturbed by, in conflict with, or wish to change their sexual orientation." That famous line from Boys in the Band, "Show me a happy homosexual and I'll show you a gay corpse," would no longer receive official sanction from the American Psychiatric Association. Homosexuals, the psychiatrists agreed, can be just as well, or just as disturbed, as heterosexuals.

Perhaps the gay credo is best capsulized by Charles Silverstein, director of the Institute for Human Identity, a New York counseling center for homosexuals and bisexuals. He calls aversion therapy "a technique of violence in the name of science, serving the same goal of social control as religious doctrine has in the past," and believes it should be banned.

"Therapists usually respond with shock at such a suggestion," Silverstein says. "They make the claim that their clients have come to them voluntarily and asked for change. What right have we, they ask, to refuse change when the patient freely desires it? It is a seductive argument, but I don't think it states the issue clearly.

"I know of no evidence that we voluntarily choose our sexual orientation, and no evidence that we voluntarily change it. To suggest that a person comes voluntarily to change his sexual orientation is to ignore the powerful environmental stress—oppression if you will—that has been telling him for years that he should change. To grow up in a family where the word 'homosexual' was whispered; to play in a playground and hear the words 'faggot' and 'queer'; to go to church and hear of 'sin'; and then to college and hear of 'illness' and finally to the counseling center that promises a 'cure'—that is hardly creating an environment of freedom and voluntary choice. The homosexual is expected to want to be changed and his application for treatment is implicitly praised as the first step toward 'normal' behavior.

"What brings them into the counseling center is guilt, shame, and the loneliness that comes from their secret. If you really want to help them freely choose," Silverstein tells psychologists, "I suggest you first desensitize them to their guilt. Allow them to dissolve the shame about their desires and actions, and to feel comfortable with their sexuality. After that let them choose, but not before. I don't know any more than you what would happen, but I think their choice would be more voluntary and free than it is at present."

Recent developments appear to be having some effect on psychologists who have used aversive techniques in the past. One is Alan J. Goldstein, a soft-spoken associate professor of psychiatry at Temple University, one of the nation's leading centers of behavior therapy research and training. Aversion therapy had played a small part in Temple's behavioral program for homosexuals who asked for help in being reoriented toward heterosexuality. It included the use of electric shock in some cases. But the aversive procedures went against Goldstein's grain and he gave them up. "I guess I was pretty naive at the time," he admits. "It was never something that I was particularly fond of in the first place. There are alternatives around which are far more pleasing, and I'm a lot more sensitive to the ethical issue involved.

"If heterosexuality isn't a viable alternative, then aversion therapy doesn't work worth a damn," Goldstein adds. "It's simply not enough to stamp out an end behavior. Whether it's homosexuality which one is seeking to change, or whether it's antisocial behavior, if alternative behaviors aren't available, punishment won't work. And when alternative behaviors are opened up, punishment is most often unnecessary. We de-emphasize the teaching of aversion therapy today. In fact, we haven't taught anyone how to use the electric shock equipment we have here for the last couple of years."

Chapter V

THE PERAMBULATOR
FETISHIST AND
OTHER TALES

It was Lola's long blonde hair that first caught Jeremy's eye. He really loved long hair but his wife insisted on chopping hers off with pinking shears. Since the birth of their second child, Myrna had taken no pride in the way she looked. Jeremy was bored with her and bored with marriage. That is where Lola came in. Jeremy had made a few feeble attempts to fight it, but his infatuation with the long-haired lovely who lived next door continued to grow.

Still, Jeremy was a proper Britisher, and the "affair," such as it was, dragged on for a year of eye contact and double entendres. It was Jeremy's rheumatism that finally turned the trick. He was laid up at home for several weeks on doctor's orders, the children were in school, and his wife working the day shift at the county hospital. Lola dropped over to give some sympathy and stayed for tea, and more. She became practically a daily visitor doing wonders for Jeremy's rheumatism, and the liaison continued for several months. Myrna knew something was wrong; their sex life was practically nonexistent and Jeremy seemed preoccupied all the time. Finally it all came out. Jeremy admitted he was unfaithful, that he had a mistress. Myrna tried to commit suicide. She thought it over though, and forgave her husband and said they could work things out. Jeremy decided that he did love Myrna, but he still was passionately attracted to Lola. He became depressed and remorseful.

In years gone by this embellished but true soap opera might have ended in some tearful scene of forgiveness, a trip to the marriage counselor, or in divorce. Jeremy, though, went to see his friendly neighborhood aversion therapists, Drs. John Barker and Mable Miller, psychiatrists at the Sheldon Hospital in Shrewsbury, England. Jeremy gave the psychiatrists photographs of the two women in his life, then sat himself in a darkened room with an illuminated screen. When Lola's picture was flashed in front of him, Jeremy received a painful shock to his wrist. His wife's photo was not accompanied by any shock, and this provided noticeable relief. The therapists also played a tape recording describing the "bad effects" of infidelity on Jeremy's marriage.

"Immediately after the first session, he developed a deep sense of guilt and broke down completely," the psychiatrists reported. "Subsequent sessions appeared less traumatic, but nevertheless left a deep impression on him." After six half-hour sessions in which Jeremy received about 60 shocks, the doctors declared him "cured." They believe unfaithfulness is a "common and fascinating problem" and say that Jeremy's success bodes well for future cases.

Is infidelity a problem worthy of a punishment cure? Just what *is* a "sex problem"? The so-called sexual revolution may be only a limited war, but evidence of its fallout is all around — just look at the smorgasbord of technique and how-to-do-it books that are available even in the supermarkets. It used to be easy to identify the "perverts." Those were the guys (or women) who whipped their wives (or husbands) and wore rubber raincoats to bed. Today, that might be the latest Masters and Johnson technique. In an age when a popular credo is, "If it feels good, do it," one man's perversion is another man's turn-on.

There are certain unusual sexual practices, however, that are disturbing enough to the individual or his partner, or sometimes even to the police, to cause people to seek some form of treatment. Acquiring and maintaining so-called deviant sexual behavior (and there is no value judgment attached to "deviance" by the author) are matters of learning. There is some strong reinforcing quality, mainly sexual gratification, that maintains the behavior despite any accompanying harassment and anxiety. In one experiment Stanley Rachman, a well-known British clinical psychologist, successfully created a mild fetish (sexual interest in an inanimate object) in a group of male volunteers in a laboratory setting. Slides of sexually stimulating women were flashed on a screen and immediately, and repeatedly, were followed by a photograph of women's boots. The men later got erections to the boots alone and this spread to other types of black shoes. There is no indication that the fetish lasted, but it leads to a question: Could similar experiments actually change sexual behavior? Could some future Isle of Lesbos require all female immigrants to undergo conditioning so that they would rather have sex with women than with men?

•

A 33-year-old Britisher was one of the first to undergo aversion therapy for sexual problems in the mid-1950s. The man was a perambulator fetishist. He got his kicks by viciously attacking baby carriages and women's handbags. The man admitted to his therapist, Michael J. Raymond, of St. George's Hospital in London, that ever since he was 10 he had received sexual pleasure through fantasies of damaging carriages and handbags. Soon he was carrying out two or three attacks a week, which got him into trouble with the police on five separate occasions. Sometimes he would splash the carriages with mud or oil, or slash and set fire to empty ones. He was content just to scratch handbags with a fingernail. The patient was married, but only could have sex with his wife with the aid of his bizarre fantasies.

Raymond believed only an intensive, around-the-clock

treatment would work. The man was hospitalized and given injections of a nausea drug, apomorphine, every two hours, day and night, for a full week. The patient was not allowed to eat and amphetamines were used to keep him awake at night. Just before the onset of nausea, the man was shown a collection of handbags, baby carriages, and photographs of both. After a break, there were five more days of treatment. Then the man was confined to his bed with the carriages constantly in the room, and the treatments were given at irregular intervals. On the ninth day he finally broke down, sobbing uncontrollably, and demanding, "Take them away! Take them away!" The man was released and continued treatment as an outpatient for six months before being readmitted for a booster session. A year later, Raymond reported, the man appeared to be doing well. He no longer was on the prowl and could have sex with his wife without the aid of the fantasies. However, six years later the problem returned, although not as bad as before. Raymond gave the man another dose of therapy.

Another British psychologist, Ian Oswald, also believes in concentrated treatment with a cartoon twist. Years ago, Fearless Fosdick, a scatterbrained comic strip cop impervious to any destructive force known to man, starred in a series of hair tonic advertisements. A bunch of baddies would tie Fosdick to a chair in a dark room and play over and over again the syrupy jingle, "Get Wildroot Cream Oil, Charlie." Naturally Fosdick, who loved the stuff, sang along. The poor crooks went batty after a couple of thousand verses and threw themselves on Fosdick's mercy. Oswald might not have been an avid reader of the Sunday funnies, but part of his therapy is definitely Fosdickian.

One of his patients, a man he calls Jim Brown, was a 22-year-old "rubberized mackintosh" (raincoat) fetishist. Since the age of seven, Brown had become sexually excited upon seeing women wearing the garments, and he used this in his sexual fantasies. He came for treatment because his bride turned down his pleas to wear her rubber raincoat to bed. This upset both of them. Several rubber slickers were hung around Brown's hospital room. Every two hours doctors gave him an injection of apomorphine. Then he stripped, donned a rain-coat, lifted his wife's mackintosh from a bowl, and vomited into the receptacle.

On the third day of treatment, Oswald decided that the routine was not enough like a real life experience, so he brought in a tape recorder and made a tape loop deliberately designed to disturb his patient. For hours on end, the machine sputtered:

> Rubberized clothing makes. . . . Rubberized clothing makes him sick. (Noise of man vomiting followed by female laughter.) Rubberized mackintoshes make him sick. (Vomit noise and female laughter again.)

Brown was nettled by the tape. During the night he became acutely psychotic and frequently called in nurses to tell them that voices on the tape were telling him to do things such as throw his teacup at a mirror. The simple phrases became distorted in his mind and he began hallucinating. He was convinced that other messages were being piped into his room. All in all, says Oswald, Brown showed the reactions of a paranoid schizophrenic. After his experience Brown wrote, "I was certain I was being used by some maniac called Dr. Oswald. I was certain that I was being made into some robot, or something similar, to carry out the will and wishes of the said maniac." This came from a man whom Oswald himself says was the only one in a series of cases similarly treated "who could be said to be of really normal personality." Despite his growing distrust of Oswald after the first night of the tape, Brown agreed to continue treatment and the recorder was turned on for part of another day. A few days later Brown was pronounced cured and sent home. Some 21 months later he remained indifferent to rubberized clothing.

Another rubber lover did not fare as well. The 32-year-old serviceman liked to be tightly enclosed in shiny, black rubber. After apomorphine injections, he tied himself up in rubber sheets or put on a frogman's suit. A tape loop was played, but

it unnerved him so much that he switched the machine off.
The next night he unscrewed the plug and removed the main
wire. The serviceman also received massive doses of the male
hormone, testosterone, and was given photos of nude females
to look at. He was released as cured, but relapsed after six
months. Uncured perhaps, but happy. Oswald says the man
discovered a London brothel that performed special services
for rubber fetishists and later "formed a friendship with a
male homosexual . . . whom he had first noticed wearing a
black, shiny rubber mackintosh in Hyde Park one fine summer's evening."

Michael Raymond and an associate treated another patient with apomorphine, this time for "pinup fetishism." The
man, a 29-year-old plumber, constantly cut out photos of nude
or scantily clad girls from magazines and hid them under the
rugs or furniture. This was not exactly pleasing to his young
wife who found the unwanted bonuses every time she cleaned
their flat. After an injection and just before the onset of nausea, the plumber was shown copies of his favorite photos.
After two treatments a day for two weeks, the man declared
himself cured of any urge to take scissors in hand, and the
outcome remained favorable at a 22-month follow-up. Raymond considered the treatment quite mild but failed to explain why he did not have his patient actually cut out photos
prior to the injections. If a male homosexual can be conditioned against approaching a man through the use of photos
of nude males, is there no danger of a heterosexual male having his ardor for women dampened with a similar technique?
In this case, however, the plumber's wife reported things at
home were "more natural in every way."

Electric shock is the main aversive weapon for use with
fetishists today. Two Toronto therapists treated two boys who
stole women's underwear from clotheslines for sexual thrills.
In the clinic the boys sat in front of a large box with two
chutes: one dispensed panties, brassieres, and the like, and
the other gave out neutral objects such as matches and pen-
cils. The boys were shocked almost every time they picked up
an item of underwear, and the shock continued until they
dropped it into a nearby box. There were no shocks for the

neutral objects. After a few sessions both boys reported they no longer had urges to pilfer underwear, and monthly booster sessions were given so they would have enough time to develop "normal outlets for the control of sexual behavior." It was a hit-or-miss attempt since no additional therapy was given to prod development along those more "normal" lines.

A possible problem in dealing with sexual disorders is how to handle masochism. Shock or other unpleasant stimuli could in themselves be a source of sexual pleasure, and increase rather than reduce the problem. Stanley Rachman and two British associates, Isaac Marks and Michael Gelder, treated a 34-year-old shoe fetishist who had fantasies of being kicked by men and women wearing boots or high-heeled shoes. He even had sexually arousing visions of being kicked to death. The man had convinced his wife to kick or stand on him occasionally, but she broke a bone in his back once and refused to indulge him after that. Intercourse always was accompanied by fetish fantasies.

The therapists devised a way to test their patient's sexual excitement. They had him twirl a lever at whatever speed he found comfortable. After his twirling became steady at about 70 a minute, he was handed his most adored fetish object, a pair of black rubber boots. The twirls spun up to about 85 a minute. The psychologists told the patient there would be random shocks, but, in fact, he received shocks every time the twirl rate exceeded the "normal" 70 a minute. Soon the twirls decreased, even in the presence of the boots, and the man said he found the shocks very unpleasant. The masochism was restricted to sexual areas, the therapists decided, and they felt safe in setting up a treatment program to shock the patient when he fantasized fetish behavior. The masochism quickly disappeared but on discharge the patient was merely neutral to the black boots. Since he did not despise them, he received booster sessions to prevent a relapse.

•

Transvestism, or wearing clothes of the opposite sex for sexual gratification, is a fairly widespread sexual peccadillo.

Though many transvestites are also homosexuals, the two do not necessarily go together. Transvestites also are different from transsexuals, who are people convinced their real gender is the opposite of what their body indicates and who seek sex-change surgery. For the most part transsexualism has been immune to any psychiatric or behavioral intervention.

In the early 1960s a team of psychologists in Surrey, England, treated transvestites using a particularly harsh form of aversion therapy. Take the case of George, a 33-year-old married son of a coal miner. George was a well-spoken athletic man (6 feet tall, 170 pounds) with a well-adjusted personality. He had been wearing women's clothes on occasion since he was eight. His wife, who only recently had learned of George's cross-dressing, urged him to seek treatment. Prior to therapy, 12 color slides were taken of George in various stages of female dress. A tape recording was also made in which the patient said, "I am George. I have now put on and am wearing a pair of ladies' panties and a garter belt," and so on, through all the items of clothing.

George was placed in a darkened hospital room and given only fluids for the first 48 hours of treatment. Every two hours, for six days and six nights, he was given injections of apomorphine, emetine, or another nausea-inducing drug. As soon as nausea started, the slides were projected and the tape recording played until George vomited or became intensely nauseous. He was kept awake with Dexedrine. George reported side effects such as headache and dizziness, and for a short time was in a state of semicollapse, but the treatment continued until he became increasingly irritable and confused and showed a rise in blood pressure. George admitted feeling a deep sense of humiliation every time he looked at a slide of himself, and eventually he had difficulty recalling the pleasurable experiences cross-dressing had brought him. Some 18 months later he reported he had not cross-dressed once since the end of treatment.

The same group of therapists later moved on to electric shock using a small room in which the floor had been turned into an electric grid, one of the favorite methods of animal researchers. Transvestites clad only in hospital gowns were brought into the room and told to start dressing in their favorite women's outfit. At some point in the dressing ritual, the patient received a signal to start undressing, either a buzzer or an unpleasant electric shock to the feet and ankles. The shock or buzzer recurred at intervals until the undressing was completed. Some 400 separate trials would be given over a six-day period. One patient, a 33-year-old civil servant, reported that he had not engaged in any transvestite behavior for six months after treatment. In certain situations, in which he formerly would have cross-dressed, he often experienced a dull pain in his testicles along with sexual tension that he relieved in "more acceptable" ways. The man had one reported relapse three months later while he was drunk, an apparent indication that the treatment was not completely successful.

Isaac Marks, Michael Gelder, and John Bancroft worked with a series of 24 patients with sexual problems, including 19 transvestites and fetishists. Their method was to administer shocks when the patients actually carried out the unwanted behavior and when they fantasized about it. Sexual arousal was measured by changes in penis size. Seven of the transvestites were also transsexuals, and at a two-year follow-up all had relapsed. Only 3 of the remaining 12 transvestites and fetishists said they had lost their deviant fantasies completely, but all reported they had diminished in frequency. The therapists count this as a successful outcome, even though they acknowledge that reduced cross-dressing was not necessarily followed by improved social or sexual relationships. Where there was no normal heterosexual behavior prior to treatment, patients were slow to develop it afterward, another indication that heterosexual behavior must be learned separately. It usually does not occur by itself.

Another method used by the Surrey, England, group employs simple words ("verbal representations of behavior") as a substitute for using actual behavior. They say the latter is both time consuming and costly. ("Our second transvestite had to be provided with literally dozens of pairs of nylons which were torn to shreds as he cross-dressed dozens of times a day.") Twenty-four words are written on a disk that is placed on a turntable. A viewing slot lets each word show for about two and a half seconds. Shocks are delivered (through specially wired shoes that the patient wears) each time he reads one of the words aloud. The last word is a "relief" symbol and there is no shock. For 21-year-old Henry, an Australian who cross-dressed about three times a week and occasionally engaged in animal intercourse, the shock-producing phrases were such things as "self as woman," "brassiere in mirror," and "sex with cow." The relief word was "masturbating" and Henry was told to masturbate whenever he felt sexually aroused. Following two weeks of treatment, Henry said he was convinced he would never cross-dress again.

•

One of the more novel forms of aversion therapy was stumbled upon by Michael Serber, then with the Temple University Health Sciences Center in Philadelphia. He was treating a 23-year-old law student who had been cross-dressing for about 10 years, and who was then dressing in his mother's underwear two to three times a week. Serber planned to use classical aversion therapy—slides of the man himself cross-dressing, followed by shocks—and set up a photographic session. As he tells it:

> I had explained the procedure to the patient and supplied him with women's lingerie so that I could begin photographing him. He appeared reluctant to begin. He said he was too embarrassed and ashamed to be observed while cross-dressing. I urged him on while taking still photographs at different stages of cross-dressing. He became markedly anxious. He flushed, felt weak, had to sit down several times. He was unable to get sexually excited in the least. He reported that the photographic session had completely "turned him off" and had changed his entire feel-

ing about cross-dressing. The session had lasted 25 minutes.

Intrigued, Serber had the student repeat the experience twice more in front of the psychologist and two associates. The young man was also asked to look at himself in a mirror. He was encouraged to proceed, but no judgmental remarks were made. At times he hesitated, cried, and asked to stop; he reported having nightmares and anxiety attacks between sessions. The urge to cross-dress, however, was gone, and remained so at a one-year follow-up. Serber then adapted his "shame aversion therapy" for use with patients who practiced other deviant acts such as voyeurism and exhibitionism. The psychologist listed two criteria for successfully carrying out the new therapy: The patient must be ashamed of his acts and desire not to be observed while carrying them out. Second, the patient must be consciously aware that he is performing the act. Later Serber realized that the therapy alone would not provide a new avenue for sexual drives, so he added "retraining" to give the patients some needed self-assertiveness and tips on heterosexual social behavior. Of a group of 15 patients, 5 who received shame aversion alone were all carrying out their previous acts within six months. Eight of the 10 patients who also received retraining were still "cured" at a one-year follow-up.

Ian Wickramasekera of the Peoria, Illinois, Mental Health Clinic has taken shame aversion one step further. He works with exhibitionists, mainly those who are neurotic, anxious, strongly motivated, and with fundamentalist religious backgrounds. They also have police records. In carrying out standard shock aversion therapy, the psychologist says he discovered that persuading even highly motivated patients to go through a step-by-step rehearsal of their exhibitionist behavior was extremely difficult. The rehearsal would make the patients shaky and nauseous and give them cramps, headaches, light-headedness, and palpitations. Wickramasekera saw this as a boon, because the patients were actively generating the aversive consequences within themselves. He theorized that

some exhibitionists are reinforced by the secrecy and ano-
nymity of their acts. Exposing themselves before an audience,
and at the same time being forced to become consciously
aware of what they were doing, would alter the "meaning"
and lessen the appeal of the act for them, the therapist guessed.

In practice the exhibitionist carries out his act before two
or three women who, he is told, know his name and have read
his case history. On cue from Wickramasekera, the women
move their eyes from the man's genital area to his eyes and
then to other parts of his body. The women remain expres-
sionless. They ask pointed questions: "What are you thinking? What are you feeling?" Since some of the patients seem
to slip into a trancelike state, they are encouraged to tell what
they are feeling and what they think the women are feeling
and thinking. A patient is also instructed "to conduct verbally
and aloud an introspective dialogue between himself and his
penis while enacting the deviation." Later he is told to give
his penis a voice so that it can tell what it is feeling and
thinking about the patient and the female observers. After
about 20 minutes of this undress rehearsal, the patient chats
with Wickramasekera alone to discuss things he might have
felt but did not mention previously. The psychologist says his
technique maintains an exhibitionist's anxiety at a high level,
disrupts fantasies of privacy, and occasionally leads to meaningful insights. The first six exhibitionists treated by this
method (none received more than four sessions) were all reported to have their habit under control at follow-ups ranging
from three months to three years.

Other successes have been reported in treating exhibitionists. B. H. Fookes, a therapist in Birmingham, England,
claims good results for six out of seven exhibitionists who
received up to 500 shocks as they exposed themselves in their
sessions once a day for two weeks. The average follow-up was
more than three years. Gene Abel, Donald J. Levis, and John
Clancy of the State Psychopathic Hospital in Iowa City, Iowa,
report initial success in treating several exhibitionists who
listened to tapes with their own verbal descriptions of events
leading up to actual exposure. The patient could avoid shock

by verbalizing and fantasizing alternative, nondeviant sexual behavior.

•

As behavior therapists started treating increasing numbers of sexual disorders, they began to notice an interesting phenomenon. In any group of people with sexual problems, it seemed that at least half of them masturbated using a "deviant" fantasy. Three British psychologists, R. J. McGuire, J. M. Carlisle, and B. G. Young, speculated that at least in some cases the deviant sexual preferences are developed through masturbatory conditioning. They see it as a three-step learning process. First, either because of some unpleasant heterosexual experience or feelings of physical or social inadequacy, a person comes to believe he cannot have a normal sex life. Then the person has an unusual sexual experience that stimulates a masturbatory fantasy. As he repeatedly masturbates to the deviant fantasy, the strength of both the fantasy and the actual behavior is increased. They cite as an example a 17-year-old boy who became sexually aroused when he saw a girl wearing only her underwear, and later frequently masturbated to that vision. After a while, as the image of the girl faded, advertisements and displays of women's underwear were enough to feed his fantasies and kill any desire for normal heterosexual relations.

The theory received some backing from work done by David R. Evans, a professor at the University of Calgary. First, he found that in a group of 52 men with sexual problems, nearly 80 percent used a deviant fantasy while masturbating. In a group of 10 exhibitionists he treated with shock aversion therapy, half used "normal" and half used deviant fantasies while masturbating. Within a month the normal fantasy group members had lost the urge to expose themselves. It took about six months for the group that used exhibitionist fantasies.

The stage was set for Gerald C. Davison and his *Playboy* therapy. Davison, a professor at State University of New York

at Stony Brook, took on as a client a Mr. M., a 21-year-old
college senior majoring in history. "I'm a sadist," the youth
told Davison. His masturbatory fantasies were exclusively sadistic (usually inflicting tortures on women) and he said he
never had been sexually aroused by any other kind of image.
The boy's dating life was practically nil because of his concern over his fantasies. Mr. M. was given instructions during
his first session to find some privacy in the dorm and start
masturbating. He was told to get an erection by whatever
means possible—undoubtedly a sadistic fantasy—and then
begin to masturbate while looking at a *Playboy* magazine photo of a sexy, nude woman. If he began to lose his erection, he
was to switch back to his sadistic fantasy, but at all costs, he
was to focus on the *Playboy* photo as orgasm approached.

During Mr. M's second session, Davison started a conversation about the social-sexual games most men play, such as
the mental undressing of attractive women. "The purpose was
to engage him in the kind of 'stud' conversation which he had
never experienced and which, it was felt, would help to
change his orientation toward girls," Davison says. Mr. M.
was told to ask a girl out for a date and change his masturbation sessions by using photos of girls in swim suits or lingerie
with the *Playboy* photo as a backup. However, Mr. M. persisted in employing his sadistic fantasies, so Davison used covert
sensitization to pair verbally unpleasantness and nausea with
imaginary sadistic scenes. After two more sessions, Mr. M.
reported that he was successfully masturbating to the bathing
suit photos and had been unable to obtain an erection to a
sadistic fantasy. Six months after he gave up sadistic fantasies, Mr. M. decided to call them back again for nine months
of additional duty; then he gave himself the *Playboy* treatment again and, "once again, it worked like a charm. I was
back in my reformed state. . . . I have no need for sadistic
fantasies. . . . I have (also) been pursuing a vigorous (well,
vigorous for *me*) program of dating," he wrote the
psychologist.

Davison says he assumes that the pairing of masturbatory
arousal with the *Playboy* picture served to replace neutral

emotional responses to the photo with intensely pleasurable sexual responses. Then the *Playboy* photo was replaced with less openly provocative female pictures. (That should please other psychologists who complained that using *Playboy* photos could turn clients into "beauty freaks.") The swim suit photos were then replaced by completely imaginary fantasies. "It was felt that more appropriate social-sexual behavior would probably follow upon a change in sexual fantasies," Davison adds.

Other therapists are now using what John N. Marquis, of the Veterans Administration Hospital in Palo Alto, California, calls "orgasmic reconditioning." Marquis believes it is important that the "approved" masturbatory fantasy be tailored to the individual. For instance, instead of having a 14-year-old boy try to fantasize intercourse, he might be told to use visions of pleasurable dancing or kissing, things with which he would be more familiar. Marquis' patients are told to masturbate to the point where they feel the inevitability of orgasm (about two to four seconds prior to ejaculation) by using whatever fantasy they find most arousing, usually the deviant one. At that point they switch to the recommended fantasy. After this has worked four or five times, the client is told to start using the appropriate fantasy earlier in the act each time, until it becomes the only fantasy used. Once the normal fantasies begin to make some inroads, Marquis often uses covert sensitization or other forms of aversive conditioning in an attempt to stamp out or at least reduce the unwanted reveries.

One of Marquis' patients was a 27-year-old technician who had a fetish for white socks and enjoyed being cursed and spat upon during homosexual relations. He had been in a mental hospital three different times for trying to molest teenage boys. A program of orgasmic reconditioning was started along with covert sensitization and shock aversion treatment for socks and homosexual situations. Within 10 days, Marquis says, the man was noticing attractive women on the street and by the end of treatment he had a steady girl friend. The man still had occasional homosexual impulses, but no interest in socks.

Therapeutic uses of masturbation appear to be increasing, both with and without aversion therapy. It is ironic, in a way, that this sexual practice which has been frowned on, discouraged, and severely punished for so long ("it'll rot your mind" is still a surprisingly widespread belief) now appears to be part of the way to help foster more personally satisfying sexual experiences. As Jack S. Annon, director of clinical training and research at the Sex Counseling Clinic of the Kapiolani Hospital in Honolulu, points out, behavior therapists do not put any value judgment on masturbation. Suggesting it to a client (if the client approves, of course) is just as valid as any other therapeutic technique. And the proper use of masturbation will not only help change sexual attitudes, but also make a person more aware of his body and its sexual responses, thus leading to the learning of new sexual behaviors, Annon believes.

•

From masturbation therapy, the leap is not that great to a Masters and Johnson type approach to unusual sexual problems with aversion therapy thrown in for good measure. Masters and Johnson became famous for having their patients bring sex into the clinic in order to work out problems directly. Robert J. Kohlenberg, a psychologist at the University of Washington, is liable to become famous (or infamous to some) for his recent work with a 34-year-old homosexual who molested young boys. At the patient's request, Kohlenberg started a program to increase the man's sexual responsiveness to adult males. His explanation for the therapy is simple and straightforward: "Adult males were chosen as the positive goal sex object because the patient's social contacts were homosexual, and heterosexual sex was not one of the therapeutic goals requested by the patient."

The client, a Mr. M., already had been arrested twice for molesting children. He claimed he became sexually aroused only by boys around 6 to 12 years old and that he actively "prowled" for sexual contacts about twice a week at playgrounds or swimming pools. Fantasies during masturbation, and also random thoughts that popped into his head several times a day, revolved around young boys. Although Mr. M. moved in homosexual circles, he became apprehensive and tense anytime a sexual encounter with an adult male appeared imminent. The patient was clearly distressed. He considered his desire for children "immoral" (not to mention dangerous) and said it had ruined his life. Three years of individual psychotherapy and a year of group therapy had not altered his desires.

Kohlenberg believed that since the child molesting could lead to harm or trauma for another person as well as dire legal consequences for Mr. M., he should start therapy by attempting to reduce the sexual arousal value of children. After several weeks of interviews, Mr. M. was given electric shock aversion treatment in conjunction with imagined scenes of prowling and thoughts of children. The shocks seemed to work for a week or so, but then the number of prowling incidents and thoughts started increasing again. Kohlenberg thinks this might have been due to an insufficient number of trials or an inadequate shock level, but instead of revving up his machine, he decided to go ahead with the Masters and Johnson phase of his program.

The psychologist instructed Mr. M. to find a suitable partner for a real-life desensitization program. Mr. M. came up with Mr. C., a 32-year-old acquaintance who was willing to give it a go out of friendship for Mr. M. Both men attended therapy sessions, which included a discussion of learning principles (so they understood the reasons for what they were doing) and instructions for their at-home encounters during the week. At first they were to give each other sensory pleasures (touching, caressing, and so on) but touching of the genital area was not allowed and sexual arousal was not a goal. Over a 13-week course of treatment, as Mr. M. became more relaxed and sure of himself, the men slowly progressed in their lovemaking. Not only did Mr. M. become sexually aroused with Mr. C., but the sexual objects in his fantasies became older and he started finding other adult men attractive enough to have sexual relations with them. At a six-month follow-up, he reported that he had not actively sought any sexual contact with children since the end of treatment and that he had become less preoccupied with, and attracted to, young boys.

The main immediate criticism of Kohlenberg's work has not been that he helped a man toward more "normal" homosexual pursuits, but that he started out with aversion therapy rather than the modified Masters and Johnson approach. In hindsight, it was the development of an alternate mode of sexual satisfaction, rather than the shutting off of the then-preferred method, that did the trick. But what if Mr. M. had asked for therapy to relieve his anxiety about his pedophilia so that he could *enjoy* molesting small boys, one psychologist asks. Hans H. Strupp, of Vanderbilt University, answers in a way by saying that although Kohlenberg went along with his client's goal for treatment, the psychologist—by not objecting —took a definite stand on the issue. "Just as children refrain from behavior proscribed by their parents if their love for them is stronger than the temptation to go against their wishes," Strupp says, "it may be said that Mr. M. became 'desensitized' to males not because he went to bed with Mr. C. or because the therapist discussed 'learning principles as related to the choice of sexual object' but because he became convinced of the therapist's interest, sincerity, and good will."

•

There is a fascinating report on the use of aversion therapy and a number of other behavioral techniques to effect a gender identity change in a transsexual—one of the few claims of success on record. Most transsexuals are men who, from a very early age, are convinced that they are really women imprisoned in mens' bodies. They engage in appropriate female behavior and almost always demand sex change operations, something that has become much more frequent in the last decade. A team at the Department of Psychiatry of the University of Mississippi Medical Center claims the first suc-

cessful change in gender identity (back to male) in a diagnosed transsexual.

The patient was a 17-year-old boy who had thought of
himself as a girl for as long as he could remember. He began
cross-dressing before he was five, had sexual fantasies of himself as a woman having intercourse with a man, and exhibited
effeminate behavior that made him an object of ridicule at
school. The boy was too young for sex change surgery, so he
agreed to a treatment program to at least make him more comfortable with himself. At the start, the therapists tried to alter
directly the boy's patterns of sexual arousal. After an unsuccessful attempt to introduce heterosexual stimuli gradually
during periods of sexual arousal, the boy was given 48 daily
half-hour aversion therapy sessions. He would imagine transsexual fantasies (similar to those that he used during masturbation), and receive electric shocks. This, too, was unsuccessful and was dropped after two months.

Next the therapists decided to modify the boy's effeminate
physical behavior (sitting, standing, and walking) toward a
more masculine direction. He was shown the "proper" behavior and, with the help of videotape playbacks, the youth was
taught to model his behavior along the lines of boys his age.
He also was taught to change the pitch and inflection of his
speech, and he rehearsed various real-life scenes such as having a bull session with the other guys or asking a girl for a
date. After nearly a year, the boy "behaved like a man, felt like
a man, and thought as a man does." However, he still was
attracted to other men, having changed from a transsexual to a
homosexual. In much the way that doctors tell patients with a
common cold that if they would only catch pneumonia they
could be cured, the therapists now felt they could go back to
earlier techniques that had failed. Arousal to female photographs was built up by introducing them in conjunction with
male photos. Then both electrical aversion and covert sensitization were administered over a two-month period. Sexual
arousal to men dropped to nearly zero while arousal to females kept increasing.

A year after the end of treatment, the boy had a steady girl friend and said that he was becoming more confident and talkative every day. It was a long, tedious process for the therapists. They had broken down the complex behavioral pattern of transsexualism into a number of different components and altered each one in turn, producing an overall change. They warn, though, that the case might have been unusual because many transsexuals, "particularly older and more sophisticated patients, refuse any treatment perceived as a threat to their mistaken gender identity." As in most other areas, the longer the behavior has been ingrained, the more resistant it is to change by any means.

•

Aversive techniques also have been used, although with less frequency, to conquer more mundane sexual problems. Dr. Myron S. Denholtz, an associate professor of psychiatry at the New Jersey College of Medicine and Dentistry, reports on the case of a 32-year-old schoolteacher who had been troubled with premature ejaculation for seven years. He was ambivalent toward his wife, feared he was homosexual because he could not perform in bed, and was terrified at the thought of becoming a father. He rapidly was turning into an alcoholic as he fortified himself before getting into bed. His wife was highly critical, intolerant, and uncooperative in the man's attempts to overcome his sexual fears. She constantly harangued him, tossing off such bon mots as, "You're not a man, you must be a queer."

Dr. Denholtz decided to use a tape-recorded "flooding" technique in which fears are presented in the imagination in such a manner and with such force that they cause maximum anxiety. Constant repetition of a fearful scene is supposed to make it easier and easier to cope with until the real-life situation itself loses its fear-producing qualities. In this case the scene was the man having intercourse with his wife. He was asked to picture himself entering her, ejaculating uncontrollably, and then being unable to pull away as she held him tightly with almost superhuman strength. The wife was said to be midway through her menstrual cycle and certain to get pregnant; in fact, Dr. Denholtz had "her" shout out, "I'm going to have a baby and you're going to be a father, *father,* FATHER. You'll have to take care of me and the baby forever." The tape recorded wife repeatedly heaped abuse on her husband.

The scene was played over and over for about a half hour, during which the schoolteacher suffered intense anxiety. The tape was repeated a week later and then the teacher was given the recording to play twice a day himself. Within two weeks, the man's fear of paternity and responsibility for children was much less and he began looking for an outside sex partner, something he had lacked the assurance to do before. Two months later, Dr. Denholtz reports, the man started a highly pleasurable outside affair and within six months he started taking steps to divorce his wife.

Chapter VI

KIDS, COMPULSIONS, AND PHOBIAS

O. Ivar Lovaas was frustrated. The UCLA psychologist had become quite attached to the pretty little blonde girl under his care; he felt almost as if she were his own child. Lovaas was trying to halt the self-destructive behavior of the disturbed youngster, and after all else failed, he decided to use a method known as "extinction." After he removed the ropes that bound the girl to her bed, she kept battering her head, raising ugly welts, and causing blood to flow. Lovaas and his staff knew that if the girl were allowed to hit herself constantly, perhaps several thousand times, the behavior eventually would stop by itself. In the meantime, however, she would hurt herself, possibly seriously. Also, the "cure" would not be effective outside the room in which she received it; if she went out into the hallway, her punching probably would start all over again.

Finally, it became too much for Lovaas to bear. Without precise scientific detachment, he slapped the girl and shouted, "Stop that!" She whirled around, startled at the unexpected twinge of pain. Her self-inflicted hitting stopped immediately and the light bulb of inspiration flashed brightly for Lovaas, making him one of the pioneers in the use of aversion therapy for children. In the last 10 years hundreds of children, ranging from infancy to adolescence, have received such treatment for psychological and even apparently physical problems that have been stubbornly resistant to change. Even that most puzzling and heart-rending childhood affliction, autism, has shown some signs of giving way a bit with the application of a package of behavior therapy techniques that includes aversion.

Using punishment on a child of below-normal intelligence and social abilities goes against the grain of everything that well-intentioned mental health workers have said for years. Smother the child with love and affection, they said, but do not be harsh regardless of how destructive the behavior or how frustrated you become. Recent studies have shown, though, that it is precisely this attitude that maintains certain behaviors in subnormal children. Having a member of the family or a nurse come running every time a child hits himself reinforces the unwanted behavior and leads to certain repetition. Lovaas is convinced that the presence of pain and anxiety in infants is essential to learning normal behavior and that the termination of pain and discomfort by parents is a vital first step in the building of social bonds. Many psychotic children do not seem to have any anxiety; in fact the less anxiety, the more severe the regression, Lovaas believes.

Autism is complex. It is not one disease or behavioral problem, but a number of possibly related symptoms including self-injury, social withdrawal, self-stimulation (rocking back and forth, flapping hands), and either an almost complete lack of speech or a mindless parroting of certain phrases. For years, a child who showed one or two of the symptoms was called "schizophrenic" or "mentally retarded" and was dealt with in special schools or institutions; a child who showed them all was labeled "autistic," and shunned even by most therapists as hopeless. The early psychiatric dogma had it that a child became autistic because his mother wished he did not exist and that he therefore turned inward. That hardly was helpful for the child or the parents.

In the mid-1960s, Lovaas and two associates, Benson Schaffer and James Q. Simmons, tried out the "pain is necessary for normalcy" theory on two five-year-old identical twins, both autistic. The boys did not speak or respond to speech. They did not recognize adults or each other. They spent up to 80 percent of their waking hours rocking, fondling themselves, and waving their hands and arms. They also threw plenty of tantrums, often throwing things and hitting themselves. Conventional psychiatric techniques had been tried for a year without success. It seemed certain that the twins faced a bleak future, so electric shock was used as a last resort to try to teach them some social behavior. The experiment took place in a 12-foot-square room. The floor was converted into an electrified grid through the use of metal tape connected to a 6-volt battery. The shock was set at a level that the therapists agreed was "definitely painful and frightening."

Two therapists faced each other about 3 feet apart with one of the twins in the middle. Whichever therapist the twin faced would say "come here," and a shock was given until the twin moved toward him or was pushed in that direction. Later, shock was withheld if a twin approached the adult, who was "saving" him from a painful situation, within five seconds after he was called. The therapists gradually moved further apart and stopped calling the child. Shock also was given any time one of the boys threw a tantrum or engaged in self-stimulatory behavior; the therapist would say the word "no" at the same time. After only three shock sessions, the twins learned to respond to the verbal beckoning. This behavior lasted nine months and when it started slipping, it was restored with one booster shock. Not only was self-stimulatory and tantrum behavior suppressed for 11 months before a booster was needed, but the twins seemed more alert and affectionate, and they sought the company of adults. In another experiment, the twins were taught to hug or kiss the therapists on command by receiving a shock to their buttocks when they did not comply. A correct response brought praise.

In separate work with other youngsters Lovaas and his associates used aversive techniques to try to manipulate severely self-destructive behavior. The children most frequently banged their heads and arms against walls or sharp corners; beat themselves about their heads or faces; and bit themselves, sometimes deep enough to expose a bone. Most of them had been in straitjackets for years or had been tied to their beds to prevent them from seriously harming themselves. The most promising and humane method to help the children would have been to build up other, incompatible behaviors to replace the self-destructive ones. This was judged not feasible because most of the children came from, and would return to, state hospitals that were understaffed and could not provide the attention and know-how for a successful follow-through. Aversion therapy seemed to be the only answer.

Lovaas and his team at the UCLA Neuropsychiatric Institute decided to put their theories to an extreme test. They asked two state hospitals to send along their worst cases of self-destructive children. Three were chosen. John, an eight-year-old with an IQ of 24, had no speech and little social behavior. Since the age of two, he had pummeled his head with his knuckles, and in the prior six months was constantly in restraints and needed continuous attention. Linda, eight years old, who had an IQ of 33, was almost completely blind. For the preceding year her wrists had been tied to her thighs to prevent further injury to her already ravaged ears. Greg, 11, had a brain disorder and was severely retarded. He needed a wheelchair since he seemed unable to walk, and had been tied spread-eagled to his bed for most of the two years before coming to UCLA.

Lovaas decided to use a battery-powered electric cattle prod to shock each child's leg when he or she started self-injurious activity. The shock, the therapists reported, was definitely painful, rather like a whip flick or a dentist drilling on an unanesthetized tooth. The change was dramatic. After only a few shocks, the hitting stopped. There was an immediate increase in social behavior such as eye-to-eye and physical contact with adults, and a decline in a number of "inappropriate" behaviors such as whining and fussing. However, one 16-year-old girl who received the same treatment later developed aggressive behavior toward other children on the ward.

Once obstructive behaviors are dealt with, children can be taught through rewards and reinforcement to become more sociable and do such things as dressing and eating for themselves, although few children diagnosed as autistic ever become completely normal. Whether or not the gains last seems to depend on what happens after the initial treatment. Lovaas charted five different behaviors for 10 children who were treated by his team and then followed up from one to four years later. Four children who were discharged to state hospitals lost almost all of their gains, but those who returned home to their parents maintained the gains or showed further improvement. (For the institutionalized youngsters, a brief reapplication of the treatment temporarily reestablished the original gains.)

Lovaas' techniques, along with several variations, have been used in clinics and hospitals around the world with mixed results. The Murdoch Center, a state hospital in Butner, North Carolina, eliminated the self-injurious behavior of a nine-year-old psychotic boy whose head banging had left him practically blind. First, human physical contact (something the boy craved) was withdrawn whenever he hit himself and reinstated when he stopped. Later shock was used to try to make the effect last longer. For a 14-year-old epileptic girl who continually fell to the floor (an action unrelated to her occasional seizures), the aversive consequences included scolding by the staff, wearing a football helmet for the day, and being isolated from the rest of the ward. The Lafayette Clinic in Detroit reported that this punishment, along with positive reinforcement, resulted in eliminating the falls after six weeks.

Mrs. Leslie Grant, the mother of an autistic child and head of the American Foundation for Autistic Children, turned engineer and developed an "electronic helmet" to stop her daughter Linda from banging her head against walls. The child wears a battery pack on her back with an electrode attached to her arm; if the helmet hits against something, a shock is transmitted automatically. Mrs. Grant keeps the equipment switched off most of the time now because the mere presence of the helmet comforts her daughter and prevents self-abusive activity, according to the Chevy Chase, Maryland, housewife.

Robert M. Browning used aversive shock as part of an overall behavior modification program at the Wisconsin Children's Treatment Center in Madison, and noted varying degrees of success with five autistic children. "It became increasingly apparent that without a highly structured program, the children would quickly retrieve previously extinguished behavior and fail to maintain recently acquired responses," he says. After 35 months of arduous work, involving thousands of trials to do away with unacceptable behavior and teach new behavior, some of the unwanted traits still came to the surface, the psychologist adds. Maintaining a child's gains after the end of treatment requires Herculean efforts which Browning thinks are beyond the ability of most parents or special schools to provide.

Getting parents involved was very much on the mind of Michael Merbaum of the Institute of Advanced Psychological Studies at Adelphi University. The crucial part of the treatment program for Andy, a 12-year-old retarded boy who would furiously beat his own face, was the training of Andy's mother to use an electric cattle prod at home after it was successful in stopping self-abusive behavior at the clinic and at a special school. The child's mother realized the value of positive reinforcement and she initiated her own behavior modification program. Over the period of a year, she used the shock stick about 25 times, mainly at the beginning of the program. After that, a strong "no" became sufficient to stop Andy's beating. The mother reported her son was "quieter, happier, and wonderful around the house." Merbaum realizes the need to exercise care in selecting the parent to administer aversion therapy. "If, for example, a parent has had a history of using punishment in a sadistic or tyrannical way," he says, "it makes little sense to encourage these methods even with close therapeutic supervision."

Some therapists have sought aversive techniques for children other than shock or nausea-inducing chemicals, either on ethical grounds or because they cannot get permission from higher authorities. A group of psychologists at the University of Mississippi treated a six-month-old girl who vomited after every feeding and whose weight had dropped to 7 pounds, 15

ounces, or an ounce less than she weighed at birth. The therapists noted that prior to vomiting, there was a characteristic
rolling motion of the tongue, and each time they saw that,
they squirted one or two drops of tart reconstituted lemon
juice from a syringe into the infant's mouth. The vomiting
stopped within a month and the infant started gaining weight.

John B. Conway and Bradley D. Bucher, of the University of Western Ontario, acted on the suggestion of the father of
a young girl and used a shot of aerosol shaving cream in the
mouth every time the child started screaming prior to a full-
blown temper tantrum. The technique later was used by the
parents. After six months, the number of tantrums declined
considerably to about one a week.

Therapists at the Edward R. Johnstone Training and Research Center in Bordentown, New Jersey, were denied permission to use electric shock on a self-injuring 13-year-old girl
and used, instead, "aversive tickling." When the girl started
banging her head, an attendant would approach from the rear
and tickle her beneath her arms in a forceful and aggressive
manner. The treatment also was tried on another girl who
attacked fellow students. The unwanted behavior of both girls
declined in frequency, but was not eliminated entirely.

•

Aversion therapy has been used with some success in the
treatment of a wide variety of neuroses, particularly obsessive-compulsive behavior and phobias. A neurosis is a comparatively mild form of mental disorder, and the person who
has one is usually aware of it and seeks help. Even a "mild"
disorder can severely handicap the person who has it, filling
him with anxiety. People who have an obsessive-compulsive
neurosis are plagued by the constant, and unstoppable, intrusion of unwanted thoughts, urges, or actions. The thoughts
often do not make any sense to the person himself; the actions
sometimes take on the characteristics of a complex ritual that
is so time consuming it becomes the focus of a person's life.

Take, for example, Mrs. M.G., a 33-year-old Montreal
housewife who suffered for seven years from horrifying (to

her) temptations to carry out aggressive and sexual acts. She was one of five patients with a long history of obsessions who were treated by Leslie and Carol Solyom and Frank T. Kenny of the Allan Memorial Institute, part of McGill University. If a patient was trying to eliminate an obsessive fear or temptation, he was asked to express it in 10 distinct phrases. Shock was given after each phrase. If the target was a compulsion or ritual, the patient was asked to break down the behavior into 10 distinct stages (steps in compulsive handwashing would range from turning on the faucet to drying the hands) and a shock was applied after each step was imagined.

Mrs. M.G. came up with phrases to be punished including: "I am going to yell that I'm going insane;" "I am going to strangle my children;" "I am going to have sex with my dog." The housewife had seven shock sessions and six months later reported that most of the temptations had disappeared. She said she no longer feared she was going insane and when she saw a belt or tie in a store, managed to stifle the desire to strangle someone. "If I go to a concert I may think 'Get up and strip naked,' but I no longer fear that I will do it," she added.

Another patient, a 37-year-old nurse, had obsessive doubts and compulsive rituals centered around the safety of other people. She constantly doubted whether she had turned on a patient's cardiac alarm or whether she had left a burning cigarette somewhere, and she always was checking up on herself. After 11 shock sessions, the rituals became difficult to carry out, but the doubts remained and the nurse felt even more anxious than before the start of treatment. The doubts were treated in six more sessions and they became much less troublesome, the Canadian therapists reported. Six months later the nurse still was improved, they said. However, the thoughts that had occupied so much of her waking hours now seemed to have switched to her dreams. She had nightmares about catastrophes at the hospital.

The five patients at Allan Memorial Institute previously had undergone another type of aversion therapy developed by Leslie Solyom, but without any long-lasting effect. A 23-year-old musician, R.B., was more successful. Solyom traces the young man's problems back to the time, two years before, when he had taken eight capsules of morning glory seeds. The hallucinogen at first relaxed R.B., then made him very introspective. He began having strange sensations, became alternately anxious and depressed, then excited and overtalkative. He was hospitalized several times, but continued to be obsessed with various thoughts and felt compelled to check his own performance constantly. He had temptations to yell obscenities, punch somebody in the nose, and urinate on the floor. Solyom had R.B. write, then tape record, a detailed description of his obsessive experiences. The tape was played back with 15-second pauses right before descriptions of the thoughts or temptations. At the end of the pause, R.B. received a shock. When he pressed a button to stop the shock, the tape started again, thus pairing relief from the shock with the thoughts that had been so disturbing. This, it was felt, eventually would make the thoughts less disturbing. R.B. had seven half-hour sessions using eight different taped experiences. Four years after his release, he still was free of obsessive symptoms.

Compulsive behavior often can be dangerous, either for the person who suffers from it or for people around him. Torkel Scholander, a Swedish psychologist, treated a 14-year-old boy who had frequent epileptic seizures and developed a habit of tying a scarf very tightly around his neck. Whenever his mother tried to stop him, he clamped both hands around his neck and sometimes stayed like that for hours. Scholander devised an automatic device that delivered shocks when the boy's hands came within a predetermined distance of his neck. The "neck grips," which had peaked at 36 per day, fell off and disappeared after a month. The boy wore the device for an additional month, and nine months later he remained free of his symptoms. Moreover, his epileptic seizures also went away, the boy's self-esteem increased, and he started dating for the first time.

Barry A. Bass, of Indiana State University, treated a 43-year-old Navy veteran who was obsessed with violence. He had impulses to drive a car into oncoming traffic, to strangle bus drivers or his wife, and to jump from high buildings or bridges. Because of the wife problem, the man had not slept in the same bed with any woman for more than a few minutes for the preceding 18 years. It was decided to attack this obsession first, and a mild electric shock was given every time the veteran conjured up an impulse to strangle his wife. A week later the patient reported that his obsessive thoughts had increased and he desperately wanted something to use at home to help him. Bass recommended that the man wear a thick elastic band on his wrist, and every time he had an impulse to strangle his wife, to snap the band against his wrist until the thought left him. After 47 weeks of band snapping, the veteran no longer had impulses to strangle his wife, although he still was obsessed with fears of harming others despite additional behavior therapy.

A 17-year-old, tenth-grade student at a vocational high school in New York, actually crossed the line from compulsive thoughts to action. The youth set fires and after starting two trash blazes in the backyard, he set fire to the family house late one night. The building was destroyed and he and the rest of the family barely escaped with their lives. At first, the boy denied setting the fire, but then admitted to Myron S. Denholtz, a psychiatrist at the New Jersey College of Medicine and Dentistry, that "voices" had told him to set it. He said he would do it again if the voices told him to do so.

Dr. Denholtz and the family took color slides of the boy setting fires in a variety of situations. They also took photographs of the family car (of which he was extremely fond) and scenes in which family members smiled at him benevolently. When the fire scenes were flashed on a screen, the boy received a painful shock; when he punched a button to end the shock, one of the family or car photos came on. Family members were taught how to carry out the treatment, and they administered it daily for 45 days, then three times a week, and, finally, every two months until two years after treatment first began. A year and a half later, there had not been any wisps of smoke in the night.

Imaginal aversion therapy has been used to deal with obsessive-compulsive behavior. A 27-year-old housewife developed a ritual for her housework. She would spend hours on a step-by-step routine of folding clothes, making beds, or putting the groceries away. She would, for example, spend 5 to 10 minutes folding each item of clothing she had washed, making sure it was completely wrinkle free. Then she would carry each item individually to a drawer across the room, carefully place it in its proper pile (and refold it again if it became wrinkled at this point), close the drawer, open it to recheck neatness, close the drawer, and go to the next item. Her therapist, Patricia A. Wisocki, decided to use covert sensitization.

The woman was told to relax and imagine scenes in which she either was thinking about performing the compulsive behavior, about to engage in it, or actually doing it. When the image was clear, she was told in graphic terms to imagine vomiting profusely all over the clothes or to see worms or maggots crawling through the clothes pile. In addition, covert reinforcement was tried. The housewife was told to imagine scenes in which she refrained from carrying out the obsessive-compulsive behavior. At that point, Ms. Wisocki would say the word "reinforcement". and the woman conjured up a predetermined pleasant scene. After 16 hours of therapy, the obsessive-compulsive behavior was eliminated and remained gone at a one-year follow-up.

Although the category of "fishwife" does not have any official psychological standing, a 45-year-old Scottish housewife who fit the description took the punishment cure at the hands of Euan L. R. MacPherson of the Royal Edinburgh Hospital. The woman had a 16-year history of anxiety and a type of hysteria that made her think she constantly had a lump in her throat, making it difficult to swallow. The woman was hypercritical and aggressive toward her husband, a mild-mannered professional man who spent most of his evenings away from home at "committee meetings." But the woman's mother, who lived with the family five days each week, dominated her. The mother decided on the week's shopping, criticized her daughter's cooking, and spoiled the couple's nine-year-old son.

The woman gave MacPherson a detailed account of situations in which she had been inappropriately overassertive with her husband or underassertive with her mother. Twenty situations were presented with alternate responses, and the woman was told to pick the response she felt was most natural. For situations involving the husband, assertive responses were followed by a shock whereas nonassertive replies were followed by the therapist saying "good." In situations involving the mother, the shock and praise were reversed. The woman received 36 sessions over six months. Halfway through, she became depressed and tearful over the "miserable life I have given my husband," and felt resentment toward her mother. There was a flare-up at home and the mother moved out. The patient started gaining back weight she had lost because of her swallowing problem. At a two-year follow-up she remained free of previous symptoms. Her husband was spending more evenings at home, her son was properly disciplined, and her mother was content to pay visits one afternoon a week.

•

If a person turns and runs after he sees a snarling lion tear across his front lawn, that is justifiable fear and common sense. If the same person does the same thing in the presence of a purring pussycat, that, in all likelihood, is a phobia. A phobia is an intense and irrational fear of an object or a situation that a person knows does not pose any real danger to him. There are many phobias. Among the most common are fear of animals (snakes and rats lead the list) and fear of spaces, either wide-open (agoraphobia) or too confined (claustrophobia). Aversion therapy is not the most widely used or preferred behavior modification technique used to treat phobias. The honors go to systematic desensitization, a technique developed by Dr. Joseph Wolpe, a professor of psychiatry at the Temple University School of Medicine and one of the founders of modern-day behavior therapy.

In systematic desensitization the patient is first taught deep muscle relaxation. Then, with the help of his therapist, he devises a list of phobic situations and places them in order of how disturbing they are. A person with a snake phobia might place seeing a picture of a snake at the bottom of his list and having a snake crawl through his hair at the top. The patient is told to relax and imagine the item at the bottom of the list, the one least disturbing, and then concentrate again on relaxing if he becomes anxious. This is repeated until the patient can imagine the scene without any anxiety. Then he proceeds, step-by-step, up the list until the entire hierarchy is free from anxiety; the effect often carries over to real-life situations.

There are a number of cases in which desensitization does not seem to work. Some people cannot master the relaxation technique and others have difficulty imagining the series of scenes. One alternate method, already mentioned briefly, is the aversion relief therapy championed by Leslie Solyom of Allan Memorial Institute at McGill University. Patients narrate on tape some of their own phobic experiences and fears. Silent gaps are put in the tape right before a particularly anxiety-provoking phrase. Before the silence ends, the patient gets an electric shock; he presses a button to turn off the shock and the relief is paired with the phrase that previously had provoked anxiety. In a study of 40 phobic patients, Solyom reported that 80 percent had lost their phobias following treatment.

Some patients suffer from a number of phobias, and a therapist usually goes after the one that is most debilitating. One of Solyom's patients, Miss K.Z., a 19-year-old office worker, had fears of darkness; enclosed spaces; elevators; open water; and animals, especially dogs and cats. The animal phobia was the worst. If she saw a dog on the street, even far away, her heart beat faster, she shook, became flushed, and felt like crying. She often would turn around and go home, even if she was on her way to work. Solyom gave the girl 10 sessions of aversion relief followed by 10 sessions of systematic desensitization. The latter sessions used photographs of dogs and cats, stuffed animals and, finally, a seven-week-old puppy. By the end of treatment she had become friendly with the puppy and could sit next to it and pet it. Two years after treatment she still was free of her most troublesome phobias.

Solyom and his associates conducted a study to compare the effectiveness of aversion relief and systematic desensitization, using 10 phobic subjects in each group. The psychologists found there was little difference in results, although hysterical patients benefitted more from systematic desensitization and patients who rated high on the obsessive scale received more benefit from aversion relief.

In their most complex project to date, the Solyom group developed a mock-up of an airplane cabin to treat 40 patients with air travel phobia. They noted that one recent study indicated that as much as 10 percent of the population has an intense fear of flying and another 20 percent has a mild fear of winging it. Their patients either avoided flying altogether or had excessive anxiety when they traveled by plane. A clinic was turned into a jet cabin with 16 standard airplane seats, equipped with finger shock devices, and a motion picture screen. The patients recorded three to five first-person accounts of past flying experiences, describing everything that made them anxious, such as the roar of the engines or air turbulence. As in previous sessions the tape was interrupted by pauses, shock, relief, and resumption of the tape. After eight half-hour sessions, a film was shown that depicted airplanes taking off and landing, activities of passengers on board, and scenes inside airports. The shocks would come before such things as a stewardess saying "Fasten your seat belts" or the pilot booming out over the loudspeaker, "Bumpy weather ahead."

The psychologists matched the aversion relief group against three others: systematic desensitization, habituation (the same as aversion relief but without the shocks), and group psychotherapy in which patients discussed their phobias, talked to an experienced pilot and finally took a 15-minute practice flight. The pass-or-fail test for all the groups after treatment was the ability to take a 35-minute trial flight and then a longer trip. The immediate effects and those a year after treatment were different. In group psychotherapy only one patient "passed" the trial flight. Eight of the aversion relief group and seven in each of the other groups passed for an overall success rate of 73 percent. A year later, to the therapists' surprise, 50 percent of the psychotherapy group were also taking flights with little or no anxiety. Based on these results, there would appear to be little need to continue shocking phobic patients since other, less offensive methods worked just as well. It remains to be seen, however, if aversion relief might provide more long-lasting results, say after 5 or 10 years.

Another aversive technique used on phobic patients is called "flooding" or "implosion." In flooding, the patient is exposed to the phobic situation for long periods without a chance to avoid it. He experiences fear at its maximum intensity until he can tolerate the situation and the fear becomes extinguished.

The London Institute of Psychiatry recommends the following imaginary scene for "flooding" a patient who has fear of heights: The patient is asked to imagine himself entering a 40-story building. As he takes an elevator to the roof garden, his mood of apprehension and anxiety increases. The patient then is taken by a friend to the edge of the garden and unwittingly leans on a brick wall that collapses. The patient falls over the remains of the wall, loses his balance, and ends up hanging by his hands from the building edge, frantically swinging 40 stories above the street. He slowly loses his grip and finally falls. The therapist describes the plunge in vivid, slow-motion detail: the impact, the crunch of breaking bones, the blood and gore. Those parts of the story that still evoke emotional reactions are repeated, with other details added until the patient's fear of heights has been extinguished.

Implosive therapy is always "imaginal." Thomas G. Stampfl, the University of Wisconsin professor who coined the term, says its goal is to reproduce, in the absence of physical pain, as good an approximation as possible of the sights, sounds, and tactile experiences that led to the phobia in the first place. This is as much of a debt to traditional psychiatry as any behavior therapist will acknowledge, since most therapists who deal with problem behavior say that knowing the cause (if there is one) is not important to achieving success. Consider the following morbidly fascinating implosive scene that Robert A. Hogan, of Illinois State University, presents to patients who are suffering from fears of rejection.

> Shut your eyes and imagine that you are a baby in your crib. You are in a dark, shabby, dirty room. You are alone and afraid. You are hungry and wet. You

call for your mother but no one comes. If only someone would change you; if only they would feed you
and wrap you in a warm blanket. You look out the
window of your room into the house next door,
where a mother and father are giving another baby
love, warmth, and affection. Look how they love the
baby. You are crying for your mother now. "Please
mother, please come and love me." But no one
comes. Downstairs you can hear your parents talking.
"Won't that kid ever shut up," says your dad. "I can't
stand him," responds your mother. "I wish he were
never born." You can hear them shouting and yelling
about you, and cursing the day you were born. You
cry, "Please, mother, please come and love me." But
no one comes. Finally you hear some steps. They
come closer, and closer, and closer. You hear someone outside your door. The door slowly opens. Your
heart beats with excitement. There is your mother
coming to love you. She is unbuttoning her blouse.
She takes out her breast to feed you. Then she squirts
your warm milk on the floor and steps in it. Look, see
her dirty heel mark in your milk. She shouts, "I
would rather waste my milk than give it to you. I
wish you were never born; I never wanted you."

Shades of Freud! There could be few people who would
not find going through that scene several times a very averse
and disturbing experience. Hogan says he places repeated emphasis on a person being cold, lonely, unwanted, and un-
loved. He also uses imagery in which an important person in
the patient's life rejects him. For psychotics, there is a bit of a
switch. The scene is a vivid account of the patient destroying
his parents' property. He throws mud on the walls, cuts up
underclothing, burns furniture, smashes the dishes, and so
forth. Then, instead of having the patient punished (a sign in
real life that the traumatic episode is over), his father walks
into the room, picks him up and shows him great affection—a
very disturbing turn of events for a psychotic individual, Hogan notes.

A case of real-life flooding for a 29-year-old English woman who had a long-standing fear of worms, snakes, "and anything that wriggles," is described by Elliott M. Antman, now at the Columbia University College of Physicians and Surgeons. The woman had nightmares of worms crawling over her body, was unable to walk in the rain for fear she might see a worm, and avoided certain garden foods like celery and lettuce. Phobic symptoms included perspiration, palpitations of the heart, a tightness in the chest, and nausea. After watching the therapist carry out the desired behavior, the patient was asked to stand about 10 feet away from a box of mud containing six worms. After one and a half hours she moved to within 3 feet of the box and another one and a half hours later she touched the edge of the box. Two and a half hours into the second session she touched the wriggling worms and in the final half hour of the session she held the worms in her hand and let them wriggle on her thigh and race through her hair. In the next session the patient dug worms out of the hospital garden. Finally, she was given a short grass snake and spent part of her final session handling it in a calm manner. Six months later most of the woman's fears remained at low levels or were completely gone.

Chapter VII

FOR FAT GAMBLERS AND BED-WETTING ADDICTS

Like kids playing with a shiny new toy, psychologists and others have applied the techniques of aversion therapy to just about every imaginable behavioral problem over the last two decades. We have seen how some initial success in the treatment of alcoholism led slowly but inexorably to the use of aversion for smoking, sexual problems, and a wide variety of neuroses. As private, profit-making behavior modification clinics started springing up in the United States and research in the field became more acceptable (and open to grants) both here and abroad, the horizons expanded to include such "big-ticket" items as obesity and drug addiction. Other widespread but seldom-mentioned problems, such as compulsive gambling and chronic bed-wetting, have received their share of attention. Even nail biting and teeth gnashing have given way before the aversive onslaught.

•

In a world plagued with starvation, too many people are fat. That is not a moral judgment. It is a statistical fact. In the United States alone somewhere between 25 and 45 percent of all adults are at least 20 percent overweight, according to the U.S. Public Health Service, which calls obesity "one of the most prevalent health problems in the United States today." Doctors agree that obesity trims life expectancy and can lead to or aggravate a plethora of diseases. Even more important to most people, fat equals ugly. That is why millions of books promoting the latest fad diets are scooped up each year and the airwaves are filled with talk about the grapefruit diet, or the booze diet, or some such.

Treatments for obesity have included medication, psychoanalysis or group therapy, and even "therapeutic" starvation. But as Dr. Albert J. Stunkard, an obesity expert at the University of Pennsylvania, observes: "Most obese persons will not remain in treatment. Of those who remain in treatment, most will not lose weight, and of those who do lose weight, most will regain it." That holds for fad diets, too. Yet the picture is not totally bleak. Behaviorists, who believe that most obesity stems from learning bad eating habits in childhood, have used learning and conditioning techniques to produce a slim frame of mind and body.

Cakes, cookies, and chocolates were Rosie R.'s downfall. They kept pulling her into the nearest bakery in Woodford Bridge, England, and finally drove her into Claybury Hospital. Rosie was 37, separated from her husband, and had been a compulsive eater for six years. Even before her husband left her, she found a respite from her frustrations and depression in the sweet delights of the bake shop. Two or three times a week she went on binges. It was "feverish excitement," she said, that pushed her to the store where she loaded up with large amounts of cakes and pastries. She often drove her car to some secluded spot and had a virtual food orgy for an hour or two until she had wolfed down every last morsel. Then she felt bloated, sick, and tired. Luckily Rosie lost her appetite for a day or two after her binges, thus keeping her weight within bounds; but the eating sprees were seriously disrupting her job and social life.

Rosie was asked to turn the treatment room at Claybury into a minibake shop. She brought in samples of all her favorite sweets. She would pick up a cake, bring it gradually to her mouth, and nibble at it. At various stages Rosie received an

unpleasant electric shock paired with a loud buzzer; sometimes the buzzer would sound without the shock. Six half-
hour sessions were held the first day, each consisting of 40 to
50 separate tries at eating. The compulsive gobbling stopped
at once, therapist B. Wijesinghe reports. Rosie was seen for
three more months in supportive therapy, and one year after
treatment still managed to avoid the temptations of the
bakery.

Noxious odors filtered through tubes into an oxygen mask
have been used by John P. Foreyt and Wallace A. Kennedy,
two researchers at Florida State University. Their arsenal includes pure skunk oil; butyric acid, which has the smell of
rancid butter or perspiration; and a number of other pungent
chemicals. Their first experimental group consisted of three
overweight Florida State University coeds and three women
from a local Take-Off-Pounds-Sensibly (TOPS) weight reduction club. There was also a control group of six TOPS volunteers. A favorite food, such as a doughnut, was placed in front
of each woman. She was told to smell it, take it in her hands,
feel it, and think about putting it to her lips, chewing it, rolling it around in her mouth, and swallowing it. When the
woman signaled she was smelling and thinking about the
doughnut, she put her nose up to the oxygen mask and was
given a whiff of one of the chemicals. After 22 sessions the
experimental group lost an average of 13 pounds. The control
group's average loss was 1 pound. About a year after treatment
began, the experimental group had put some weight back on,
but still remained about 9 pounds lighter. The control group
had gained an average of 1 pound. Foreyt and Kennedy attrib-
ute at least part of their success to the women's strong, positive relationship with the therapists, who continually insisted
that they lose weight.

One of the more unusual aversive stimuli, cigarette
smoke, was used by Kenneth P. Morganstern. He treated a
24-year-old, 180-pound Pennsylvania State University coed
who gobbled down 200 pieces of candy and dozens of dough-
nuts and cookies a week. She ate pizza and ice cream at least
once a day, and sometimes as often as three times each day.
The prospect of electric shock frightened her, so Morganstern
decided to pair puffing on a cigarette with chewing a piece of

candy. After a long drag, the coed, a nonsmoker, had to spit out the candy and say, "Eating this junk makes me sick." So did the cigarette smoke; it led to nausea and dizziness. The girl practiced twice a day at home and used the technique in real-life situations when she felt herself tempted. At the end of 18 sessions she had lost 41 pounds, and six weeks later had shed another 12 pounds. There was no follow-up, however, and Morganstern admits he was disturbed somewhat about using cigarettes. He feels, though, that there is little chance that a nonsmoker will pick up the habit in the course of such therapy, "just as it seems unlikely that subjects would embrace electrical stimulation as a pastime" after undergoing shock treatment. Of course, the surgeon general has not declared electric shock to be habit forming and unhealthy.

By far the largest application of aversion therapy to obesity is through verbal imagery or covert conditioning, sometimes together with an actual prod. Two patients at Montreal's Douglas Hospital were treated by the combination method, covert sensitization plus the rotten-egg smell of hydrogen sulfide, when they imagined tempting foods. The first patient, a 400-pound, 31-year-old man, lost 75 pounds during 18 weeks of treatment but failed to come back for booster sessions and regained 50 pounds within four months. The second patient, a 31-year-old nurse who weighed 308 pounds, lost weight more gradually but managed to shed 75 pounds in 40 weeks.

An experiment at Arizona State University tends to show the effectiveness of covert sensitization, at least over the short term. Eighteen undergraduates ranging from 2 to 149 pounds overweight were assigned randomly to one of three groups: no action; discussion; and covert sensitization. The covert group was given three types of scenes to imagine. In the first, the student vomited just as he was about to eat a forbidden food. Next, he ate a diet meal, enjoyed it, and felt proud of himself. In the third sequence, he approached a forbidden food and felt ill, then turned away and felt better; he also felt tremendous pride for having resisted the temptation. Immediately after treatment, the no-attention group showed a mean loss of 4.5 pounds; the discussion group, a loss of less than a pound; and the covert group, a loss of 9.5 pounds. Six weeks later only the covert group had lost more weight.

Some people have stumbled upon covert conditioning by themselves. In a recent book, *How to Save Your Life,* the formerly fat news editor of WNBC-TV in New York, Earl Ubell, tells how he developed his own behavior control diet. It involved coming up with an unpleasant thought after being tempted; stopping any thoughts of eating (just by saying "Stop!"); putting a halt to getting up and actually eating the food, often by doing something else (like picking up a book); and then conjuring up a really pleasant thought to reward himself. Ubell points out that both the punishing and rewarding thoughts should have a high degree of personal relevance. For punishment, he used the unforgettable scene of seeing his father's face just a few minutes after the overweight man died of a heart attack; for a reward, he thought about a much-desired trip to Europe. The method helped Ubell lose 25 pounds the first time around, and when he later started regaining weight, he successfully used it again.

•

After the Civil War and up to the turn of the century, nearly 1 in every 300 Americans used an opium drug regularly. It was legal then, even prescribed by doctors for its soothing qualities. The danger of addiction was slow in rearing its head; it was not until 1898 that heroin was first produced. Today, narcotic addiction is widespread. The cost is huge, both socially and financially. In 1973 the government estimated there were more than 600,000 narcotics addicts in the United States and up to 2.5 million people who chronically used barbiturates or other sedatives. Some 5 million people took amphetamines without prescription, and about 500,000 were on hallucinogens or other nonnarcotic drugs. The street cost of heroin alone runs to more than $13 billion a year and about twice that amount in property is stolen to pay for habits.

Behavior modification arrived on the drug scene fairly recently and there are not yet many examples of its use. The examples of aversion therapy are even fewer, although at least one survey includes some techniques used by Synanon, the live-in group therapy centers. "If a member engages in drug use while in residence, aversive verbal stimuli may be applied, consisting of ridicule, cross-examination, and hostile verbal attack," says David C. Droppa, who works in a drug rehabilitation center in Pittsburgh. Members who even talk about drugs or who write drug-related poetry are also subject to verbal attack and ridicule.

A few researchers have tried to fight fire with fire. M. J. Raymond, then at Netherne Hospital in Coulsdon, England, treated addiction to Physeptone, an addictive stimulant, with injections of nausea-inducing apomorphine. The latter drug rarely produces addiction itself, but has been rejected by most therapists because of its hypnotic effect. Raymond's patient was a 30-year-old woman who had been addicted to Physeptone for six years. She was injected with the apomorphine, and just before the onset of nausea, she injected herself with gradually smaller amounts of Physeptone. After eight days the treatment had to be stopped because of the woman's severe depression, and three weeks of electroconvulsive therapy were ordered. The aversion treatment then was continued and after five days the woman smashed her syringe. She was discharged seven weeks later and two and a half years after that she still was free of her addiction.

Similar therapy was tried at the Boston State Hospital Drug Addiction Center. After a dose of apomorphine, the patients gave themselves a fix of morphine, enough to produce a "rush" but not sufficient to bring on euphoria or sedation. Sometimes a patient had a choice between the fix and a half hour of smoking and amiable conversation with the therapist. A 24-year-old laborer reported he was free of drug craving after treatment but relapsed when subjected to stress. A 38-year-old divorcee, a heroin addict for five years, fared better. After discharge she received some booster sessions and other supportive outpatient treatment. A year later she still was drug free.

Joseph Wolpe, one of the fathers of modern-day behavior therapy, devised a self-administered electric shock program for a physician who had become addicted to Demerol, which he used originally to alleviate severe stress. About once a week the doctor gave into an irresistible craving to take 1,000 to 1,500 milligrams of the drug, which was some 20 to 30 times the therapeutic dose. The doctor was given a portable shocker and told to use it every time he felt the craving begin. The treatment seemed to work and after a month he was given other behavioral training to deal with his underlying neurosis. After two more months, however, he resumed Demerol injections in stressful situations.

A 21-year-old college senior in Miami who was addicted to morphine was given relaxation and self-assertion training followed by electrical aversion. Shocks were administered at each of five key steps in the process of injecting himself with narcotics; some of the steps were imagined but others were actually carried out. Ten months after the twenty-fourth and final aversive session, the youth still had not taken hard drugs, although he occasionally smoked marijuana. Therapists at Boston City Hospital have reported some success with a program using covert sensitization along with electric shocks to all parts of the body where the patients conceivably could inject themselves.

Dr. Paul H. Blachy, of the University of Oregon Medical School, refined the shock technique to perhaps its ultimate in automation. He modified a normal plastic syringe by adding a photocell. Whenever an addict fixes up (a salt water solution is used) and starts to press the plunger, he receives a sharp jolt to the muscles of his forearm, and this completely stops any further pressing of the plunger. The patient performs for a group of fellow addicts seated in a circle around him. All of the addicts are hooked up in series like the twinkle lights on a Christmas tree. When the addict in the center does his thing, *all* the patients get shocked.

A treatment using covert conditioning alone was tried on a 26-year-old college graduate who had developed a habit needing 20 bags of heroin a day. Since the idea of vomiting was positively associated with a good grade of heroin, a different aversive stimulus was needed. In this case psychologist Patricia A. Wisocki used scenes of the man being attacked by a swarm of wasps or spiders, contracting instant leprosy, or being thrown into a vat of sewage. After 12 sessions in which other behavioral techniques were also used, the patient said he was determined to stay off drugs and felt confident he could handle his other problems. He was still avoiding heroin some 18 months later.

"The Gambler!" What delicious mental pictures that
phrase calls up. Yancey Derringer dealing five card stud as the
River Belle Queen paddle wheels its way up the Mississippi.
Bat Masterson, his hand never too far from his Colt .45, taking
a peek at his cards while the crowd at the Tombstone Saloon
gathers round in hushed admiration. The suave, handsome
Robert Redford type, not a hair out of place and no sign of
emotion as he calmly peels $1,000 bills off the top of a 2-inch
thick stack at the elegant baccarat table at Monte Carlo. How
magnificent; how admirable; how macho! How phoney. Gambling may be glamorous in fiction and dreams, but in the hard
light of day Glitter Gulch shows itself to be made of the
basest, and costliest, fool's gold.

Somewhere between 6 and 10 million Americans are
chronic and compulsive gamblers. Great Britain has as many
as 1 million and the problem is of epidemic proportions in
Australia. Many people gamble, both legally and otherwise,
with no ill effects except frequently empty pockets. The gambling addict, however, makes it the center of his life. He regularly gambles more often and loses more money than he
intends to, with serious personal and financial consequences.
Freud equated gambling with masturbation and said losing
(something he thought most gamblers subconsciously desired) was self-punishment for deeply suppressed oedipal
feelings. That may seem laughable today, but the problems of
"pathological gambling" have received scant medical and social attention in the years since Freud's pronouncement.

C. Philip Seager, of Sheffield University in England,
treats compulsive gamblers (mostly horse race bettors)
through electric shock aversion. By the time he sees most of
his patients, they are heavily in debt and some have been
jailed on charges of stealing. In an article in the *British Journal of Psychiatry*, Seager discerned a certain pattern of gambling behavior among his clients:

> The patient would have obtained money from some-
> where and spent it all in the betting shop on a partic-
> ular day, leaving at the end of the day's racing with
> virtually no money in his pocket. He would return

home blaming himself for his recklessness and during a tearful scene with his wife would promise never again to be so foolish and would swear to give up all gambling activities. The next morning he would pick up the morning paper and turn to the racing page. There he would see one or more runners which he would identify as absolutely certain winners, which would solve all his financial difficulties and allow him to regain his standing and self-respect. He would usually not ask his wife for money but would borrow or obtain in some other way sufficient resources to return once more to the betting shop to try his luck. Almost always, of course, he would lose and so the circle would be completed.

Seager is convinced that the start of the cycle of unwanted behavior is seeing the list of sure-fire nags trumpeted in the morning newspaper, and this is what he tries to eliminate. A pile of newspapers is placed in front of the client. The papers have been doctored so that racing news comes up every fourth page. When the page comes into view, the patient is shocked until he discards it. Other clients who get their information from the betting shops (legal in England) are shown photos of such shops, lists of races, and racing tickets. In a group of 16 patients, five remained free of gambling at follow-ups ranging from one to three years. Another patient denied gambling, but Seager had some doubts; a seventh patient was making occasional small wagers well within his means. All patients were offered supportive psychotherapy and were referred to Gamblers Anonymous, which is patterned after Alcoholics Anonymous.

A Royal Air Force psychologist, A. B. Goorney, also uses electric shock, but believes it must be directed at all stages of the gambling behavior. In treating one 37-year-old man who had a 13-year history of compulsive horse race betting, Goorney applied random shocks five times during the day: in the morning while the patient read the racing pages and made his selections; three times during the day when the man imagined betting behavior or while he watched televised races; and in late afternoon when he listened to race results on the radio. In 45 sessions the gambler received 675 shocks. He became anxious and angry at the therapist, but continued treatment. More than a year later he had no desire to place bets and no interest in horses.

In Australia, where gaming clubs are a way of life, K. M. Koller of St. George Hospital in Kogarah has treated poker-machine addicts. Patients were given shocks randomly while they played on their favorite brand of poker machine, using real money, in a hospital ward. The technique and Koller's description of the wretchedness of some of his clients make it clear that he could just as well be referring to the scores of men and women who become hypnotized by slot machines in Nevada and stand around for hours feeding their nickels, dimes, and quarters down the voracious slots. Some six months to two years following treatment, half of Koller's 12 patients were not playing the machines or played them only occasionally. The patients who did best appeared to develop a dislike for the poker machines early in treatment. They were the ones who were determined to win at gambling, rather than those who usually expected to lose. They also were more stable, apart from the gambling problem, than the failures. Many clients felt that just seeing the money disappear so rapidly down the slots, and being aware of it for the first time in their lives, was a startling and beneficial part of the therapy.

Shock was used as part of an overall therapy program for a 32-year-old Los Angeles man who went on binges at a local poker club about every three months. The outbreaks lasted three to five days and the man would stay at a club until it closed at 4 A.M. or until he had lost all his money. Sherwin B. Cotler, of the Center for Behavior Therapy in Beverly Hills, instructed the man to substitute other activity such as golf or a ball game for his poker club visits. He was told to keep detailed records of his gambling activity to make him aware of some of its more negative aspects. Then when he visited the club, he took along only a certain amount of money and, using a portable shocker, jolted his hand just before gathering in chips on a winning round. The client also was given shocks during covert sensitization to gambling scenes and received therapy for his marital problems. After 16 clinical sessions, gambling had dropped to zero, but the man relapsed nine months after treatment began. He reentered therapy and gambling again stopped.

•

It was all an accident. Dr. M. Pfaundler, a German pediatrician around the turn of the century, was merely trying to devise a way to tip off nurses that an infant needed changing. He rigged a device consisting of two pieces of tinfoil surrounded by cloth. When the cloth became wet, the tinfoil circuit was completed and rang a bell that was attached by some wires. Dr. Pfaundler also put the devices in the beds of young patients who were enuretic, that is, bed wetters. Surprisingly he found that if the device was used for a month or so, it had distinct therapeutic effects. In some cases the bedwetting would stop just because of the child's knowledge that any incident would start a bell ringing. Two French doctors also reported success with Dr. Pfaundler's device and noted that even if a child did not wake up at the sound of the bell, the urination would almost immediately stop because of a vigorous contraction of the sphincter muscle.

Possibly because the Pfaundler device was inefficient and cumbersome, it faded into obscurity. It was not until the post-Pavlov team of O. Hobart and Willie Mae Mowrer came up independently with a similar device in the 1930s that this aversive method for curing bed wetters caught on. Although it is rarely talked about, bed-wetting seems to be a fairly widespread problem. One British survey indicated that more than 10 percent of children at age 4½ are chronic bed wetters, and about 2 percent at age 15. The problem may affect more adults than suspected, possibly as much as 1 to 3 percent of the population according to American and British surveys. For certain groups, such as old people in hospitals, the incidence is even higher and ranks as one of the aggravating problems in a ward.

The Mowrer device, which served as a model for the dozen or so commercial products on the market today, consisted of two thicknesses of heavy absorbent cotton fabric separating two large pieces of bronze screening, one of which is covered by another piece of cloth. The child sleeps directly on the pad. Within two or three seconds after urine strikes the pad, the bronze screens form a contact and short circuit, causing an electric doorbell to ring. The child is told to get up immediately and go to the toilet the moment he hears the bell; it is sometimes necessary to wake him up and give him a gentle shove in that direction. The Mowrers indicated that good results would be forthcoming within a month or two, and in a classic 1938 study they reported a 100-percent success rate with 30 children who were checked up to two and a half years later.

Other researchers have not been as optimistic about the method as the Mowrers. Although several large-scale studies came up with initial success rates of 66 to 80 percent or higher, there have been a large number of relapses. British psychologist S. H. Lovibond reported a relapse rate of up to 45 percent over a two-year period. Others blame failures and perhaps some of the relapses on such things as a lack of parental cooperation, overcrowded living conditions, or faulty equipment. A study at the Enuretic Clinic at the Royal Belfast Hospital for Sick Children in Ireland, indicated that a relapse is less likely if the treatment is continued at least four weeks after the last sign of bed-wetting. In a series of 200 children there was a 66-percent cure rate with a follow-up of more than two years. The researchers also noted that if a child has not improved after four months, the likelihood of a cure is small.

Some researchers have tried to augment the pad-and-bell method. An Australian therapist, N. D. Crosby, added a mild electric shock across the lower back and reported seven of his nine patients became dry and another was "almost cured." Later studies did not find electric shock any more effective than a bell. Portable "buzzer pants" have been developed for day as well as night training. In several studies children have been given such stimulants as Dexedrine and Methedrine just before they go to sleep on a pad. Although the use of such drugs is questionable in itself, at least one report indicates their use also greatly increases the number of relapses.

A group of psychologists at the Kalamazoo Valley Intermediate School District came up with another addition. In dealing with a mentally retarded and otherwise handicapped eight-year-old boy who was not responding to the bell and pad, the psychologists recommended that the buzzer be placed in the parents' room. When it rang, the boy's mother got up, took him to the bathroom, and immediately dunked him into a bathtub of cold water. The youngster would cry and the mother would "convey mild disappointment." If the boy had a dry night, the entire family would praise him at the breakfast table the next morning. (Other psychologists agree that there have to be "rewards" in addition to the aversive properties of the bell-and-pad set-up.) After 22 nights of cold dunks, bed-wetting was eliminated, although the procedure was used for another two weeks. In the next 18 months the child wet his bed only once. The same therapy was tried on the boy's normal four-year-old brother with some initial success, followed by a relapse.

Two British psychologists, G. C. Young and R. T. T. Morgan, recommend an "overlearning technique" following success with the bell-and-pad method in an attempt to make sure the new behavior lasts. The child must drink up to 2 pints of liquid immediately before going to bed and stay dry for 14 consecutive nights. They report that of 344 children, 10 percent who underwent "overlearning" relapsed compared to a 29-percent relapse rate for those who did not drink the water.

In one of the few attempts to stop bed-wetting among older and chronic patients, John M. Atthowe, Jr., of the University of Montana, reported success with 12 patients, half of whom were lobotomized and all of whom were labeled chronic schizophrenics. Their ages ranged from 42 to 77 and they had been hospitalized for at least 20 years. The program had four aversive features. The 12 were moved to a large and crowded 30-bed wing of the ward; lights were turned on for 10 minutes, four times during the night; the patients had to go to the bathroom at those times whether or not they were wet; and they had to listen to "aversive comments" from other patients in the wing who did not like being awakened. The program continued nightly for two months at which time those patients who did not wet their beds during the night were awarded a token which could be exchanged for some treat or special privilege. After they remained dry for a week, the patients' trips to the bathroom were eliminated and they were given the chance to move to better sleeping quarters. Some of the patients required seven to eight months of treatment, but all eventually eliminated bed-wetting. After 43 months, the seven patients from whom information could be obtained still were doing well.

•

Do you bite your nails too much? Gnash your teeth at night? Break out in itchy splotches? Do you have problems holding your urine when you laugh, or urinating at all in a public restroom? These and many other conditions are being treated today by aversion therapy. There seems to be no limit to the use of aversive techniques. Name a behavioral problem (and some that are not so obviously behavioral) and a therapist either has attempted the punishment cure on it or would be willing to give it the old college try.

Working under a National Science Foundation grant, Bradley D. Bucher of UCLA supplied portable shock machines to 20 students who were chronic nail biters. (According to one study, the average incidence of nail biting among college students is as high as 24 percent.) A student was told to shock himself as soon as he placed a finger in his mouth or on his lip. To make sure the attitude of cooperation was not also shocked out of existence, Bucher says he supplied positive reinforcement through his constant encouragement. Nine of the students reported biting stopped after the first day and four others stopped after four days. However, there were a number of relapses and dropouts, and the follow-up results are not clear.

The case of teeth gnashing and grinding at night (called "bruxism") is more serious than it sounds. It frequently can lead to serious tooth disorders and tissue damage. Two professors at the University of Virginia at Charlottesville, Robert F. Heller and Harold R. Strang, devised a Rube Goldberg set-up for a 24-year-old graduate student who had been grinding his teeth nightly for a number of years. A voice-operated relay picked up the grinding sounds while the student slept and passed on the information to an electronic counter. If there were more than three gnashes per five-second period, a loud blast of sound was transmitted through a tiny speaker in the student's ear. The grinding behavior was reduced considerably, although not eliminated. Surprisingly, the student reported that he was not fatigued on the mornings after his treatment.

A 22-year-old student at Pennsylvania State University had a long history of skin problems. In the preceding two years it had worsened because of his uncontrollable scratching, particularly at night. Richard G. Ratliff and Norman H. Stein administered electric shock every time the student scratched any part of his body. The shock was terminated when he stopped scratching and said aloud, "Don't scratch." After the end of the third session, scratching was eliminated almost completely in the clinic and for about 24 hours after each session, but persisted the rest of the time. The patient then was trained to use relaxation techniques whenever he was tempted to scratch. His problem vanished after five weeks and remained gone six months later.

"Giggle micturation" is a disorder in which people can not help but urinate when they giggle. The laughter is usually of an uncomfortable kind, associated with aggressive or confused feelings. A 22-year-old British coed urinated in embarrassing circumstances several times a week and when she was really anxious (during final exams, for instance), the incidents would happen two or three times a day. D. W. Millard, then at Queen Elizabeth Hospital in Birmingham, developed a portable device that the young lady strapped around her waist under her clothing. An electrode in the genital area would trigger two shock electrodes when just a small amount of urine was voided. The coed wore the device constantly for 10 weeks and was dry for more than six months. She then relapsed under pressure, wore the device for another month, and remained dry for more than a year.

The opposite problems, a severe case of the "bashful bladder syndrome" in which a patient cannot urinate at all or under certain circumstances, was treated at the University of Florida Health Center. The patient was a 27-year-old woman who had a long history of urinary retention and frequently had to be catheterized. Electrodes were attached to the woman's legs when she was seated on a toilet. For about 60 seconds the shock level would be increased gradually until the pain became intolerable and the woman became tense and uncomfortable. After one unsuccessful attempt, she was able to relax at the end of the shock and urinate. The woman was taught to use the shock device herself. She also was taught how to be more assertive in her behavior to deal with problems at home. Some 18 months following treatment her urinary problems had not returned.

Automatic shock collars and headgear have been used to treat a condition known as spasmodic torticollis ("wry neck") in which a disorder of the neck muscles results in abnormal movements or positioning of the head. If a patient's head is in the "wrong" position, he gets a constant shock until he moves it. Aversive shock also has been used to treat writer's cramp and is applied as soon as the tremors and spasms start. Although one early study claimed a high rate of success with the method, later research has not been able to duplicate the feat. In some cases, the symptoms were actually made worse because of the extra anxiety arising from the shocks. Stuttering has been treated with electric shocks and loud noise. There are indications that aversion might have a role in treating stutterers, but other behavioral methods are receiving more attention now.

Some problems, which at first blush might appear to be physiological in nature, turn out to be behavioral. John T. Watkins of the University of South Dakota treated a 14-year-old boy who weighed just 45 pounds because he vomited after every meal and sometimes between meals. The youngster was severely retarded and had been institutionalized for six years, often suffering from anemia and dehydration. Watkins decided to use a Hot Shot brand electric cattle prod. The boy was shocked on the cheek whenever he was seen to be rolling food in his throat (an event that usually preceded vomiting), or shocked on his hand when he tried to gag himself. The prod can deliver an incredibly high, and potentially dangerous, shock of 400 to 1,000 milliamperes, so "special precautions" were taken, including locking up the prod when it was not being used. Watkins says it might have been a good idea to have had attendants log each time they used the prod and the reason for it, but this was not done. The boy, however, suffered "no detectable undesirable side effects" and after seven weeks of constant monitoring, the vomiting declined to a level of about twice a week. The boy's weight rose 62 percent after five months.

Doctors at the Children's Asthma Research Institute and Hospital in Denver were presented with a puzzle in the form of Marvin, a 15-year-old boy who had suffered from a chronic, debilitating cough for 14 months prior to admission. During his first stay at the hospital he did not cough at all and was released after eight months. Once at home, the boy's cough returned and became so severe that he had to be readmitted to the hospital. The doctors determined that the cough had a psychological origin and was triggered by a variety of items at home such as the odors of beef grease, shampoo, hair spray, and bath soap. The cough, they realized, had been reinforced by the attention Marvin got from his family.

The therapists began a simple punishment program in which Marvin took a whiff of the things that made him cough and received a painful shock each time he responded. Instead of declining, the coughs increased and Marvin expressed considerable hostility at the treatment. The doctors then tried a new approach. They told Marvin he could avoid being shocked if he held off coughing for a few seconds. The intervals were slowly lengthened until after 75 trials (and 24 shocks) coughing to the odor of shampoo was eliminated. When Marvin expressed further hostility, he was given reassurance and encouragement to continue, and he made rapid progress with the other stimulants. Marvin was able to resume an active life. Some 18 months after treatment the cough still was absent and the boy's mother reported that her son was no longer a hypochondriac.

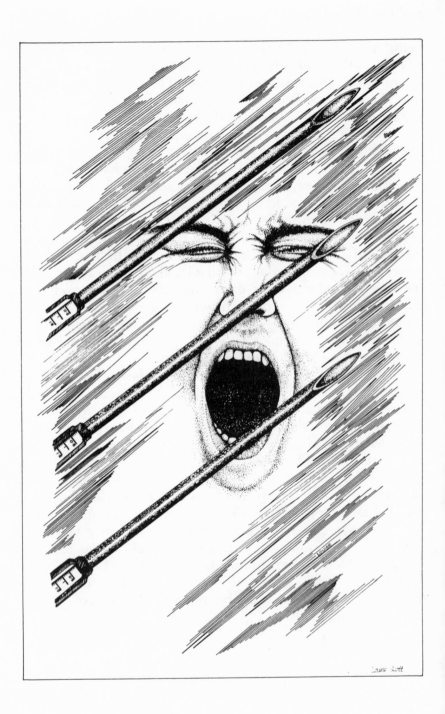

Chapter VIII

SCARING THE
DEVIL OUT

The prison is a moral hospital, the inmates the morally diseased. It is the duty of the prison to cure.
Memoirs of Gideon Haynes (a Massachusetts
prison warden), 1868.

The sensational headlines began appearing in underground publications in 1970. "Atascadero: Dachau for Sex Offenders"; "Vacaville— Legal Torture"; " 'A Clockwork Orange:' It's Not Fiction." Even the respected *Medical World News*, a weekly magazine for physicians that broke the story, called its account, "Scaring the Devil Out." They all were referring to the same thing. From the mid-1960s, and lasting for about four or five years, two California penal institutions had been using a particularly harsh form of aversion therapy on inmates, one which employed a drug that paralyzed the body and stopped breathing for up to two to three minutes. A storm of protest followed the almost chance discovery of the treatment, marking the first real public outcry against aversion therapy.

The treatments at the two California institutions were halted, but aversion therapy in other forms is widely used today in state prisons and mental hospitals. There have been some changes. Wardens and health care professionals are only too aware of the need to keep up a good public relations front, and many are reluctant to admit that they are using aversion therapy or to discuss its ramifications. Others have abolished the words "aversion therapy" but have kept the techniques, preferring to call it something like "negative reinforcement." In a setting in which a prospective "patient" is denied most freedom of movement or choice, treatment that normally would not be considered aversive could take on such a tone. Precisely because of this lack of freedom, many behavior therapists themselves go along with the belief that there cannot be any such thing as fully informed and voluntary consent to treatment in an institution. They have either decried the use of aversion therapy altogether in such settings, or have called for new procedures to safeguard inmates as much as possible.

Aversion therapy is not the only behavior modification technique, or even the one most widely used in prisons and mental institutions today, but it is certainly the most controversial. Prisoners have filed suits to block it and, at least in one case, were partially successful. Several state legislatures have toyed with the idea of banning or severely limiting institutional aversion therapy. A federal agency cut off grants from all projects employing aversive techniques and the head of the Federal Bureau of Prisons has had to deny repeatedly to a dubious Congress that federal prisons use, or ever plan to use, aversion techniques. Punishment, even in the guise of therapy, has no place in such institutions today, some say.

Others disagree. James V. McConnell, a professor of psychology and psychiatry at the University of Michigan, is a firm believer that the techniques of the modern behavioral scientist should be applied to prisoners. Yet the professor is somewhat gun-shy about expressing his views ever since a speech before a group of lawyers was condensed into a popular magazine article titled, "Criminals Can Be Brainwashed— Now!" Since then, McConnell says, he has been bombarded by people who quote him out of context and "try to make me into some kind of ogre." With some urging, he agrees to clarify his views.

"I don't think the Constitution of the United States gives

you the right to commit a crime if you want to," McConnell says. "Maybe it ought to be that you are free to act criminally if you're willing to accept the consequences, but as written, the Constitution does allow the government to prevent certain types of crimes if it can. Therefore the Constitution does not guarantee you the right to maintain inviolable your criminal personality, if you happen to have one. The question is, what should we do with you if you do have a criminal personality? Punish you or try to change you?

"I believe the day has come when we can combine sensory deprivation with drugs, hypnosis, and astute manipulation of reward and punishment to gain almost complete control over an individual's behavior. We'd assume that a felony, once committed, was clear evidence that the criminal had somehow acquired a full-blown social neurosis. Rather than trying to beat the criminal into submission—which seems immoral to me, and doesn't work very well besides— we'd try to reeducate the person; give the person the insight and social skills needed to get what he wants in a positive and humane way.

"We'd send the criminal to a rehabilitation center rather than a prison," McConnell adds, "and try to reward the person for individual growth and maturity rather than punishing the person to 'purge his soul.' From my dealings with many dozens of prisoners, I suspect most of them would welcome this alternative and would profit from rehabilitation. Perhaps in one case in a thousand we might have to restructure the person's entire personality, in which case we perhaps could use a kind of 'positive brainwashing.' "

•

The so-called "clockwork orange" treatment in California involved the drug succinylcholine (under the trade name Anectine) which, as we have seen, was used by several therapists for treating alcoholics. In normal usage the drug is a muscle relaxant employed by anesthesiologists before some operations and also in conjunction with electroconvulsive therapy (ECT). When strong shocks are applied to the head in ECT, with the express purpose of causing convulsions and blackouts for therapeutic purposes, the muscles contract so forcefully that a patient's bones could be broken under the strain unless the muscles are turned into Play-Doh. (Succinyl-choline had some public notoriety during a famous murder trial in the mid-1960s in which Dr. Carl Coppolino, an anes-thesiologist, was convicted of using an overdose of the drug, which vanishes without a trace, to kill his wife.) In aversion therapy, when injected intramuscularly in doses of 20 to 40 milligrams, the drug causes complete muscle paralysis, a halt in breathing for up to three minutes, and, to quote one practi-tioner, "an extremely negative experience." The subject re-mains completely conscious throughout, very much aware of the frightful sensations, and is therefore susceptible to suggestions and conditioning, therapists report. In rare cases the drug has reportedly caused glaucoma.

The Anectine treatment was first used around 1966 at the Atascadero State Hospital, a maximum security institution housing what California calls "mentally disordered sex of-fenders," as well as people adjudged criminally insane. The institution, which holds about 1,200 men, is run by the state's Department of Mental Hygiene. Anectine was also used for several years at the California Medical Facility at Vacaville, a psychiatrically oriented prison under the control of the Cali-fornia Department of Corrections. Altogether, there are rec-ords of 154 inmates who were involved in the Anectine programs from 1966 to 1969. Some of the men were only threatened with an injection and never received one. Most of the 64 men at Vacaville signed a consent form although at least five were forced into the program against their will. Atas-cadero did not bother with the niceties of a consent form, so it is impossible to say how many, if any, of the 90 inmates were "volunteers."

The most detailed description of the Vacaville program comes from an unpublished study by Arthur L. Mattocks, a clinical psychologist and supervisor of the research unit there, and Charles Jew, an assistant social research analyst. "There is," they said, "evidence to support a cautious, critical attitude toward the use of punishment as a means of altering behavior. This perhaps is even more true in the consideration of aver-sion therapy as a mode of treatment with aggressive, acting-out individuals than with alcoholics or sexual deviates." Most of their subjects, they said, "could be characterized as 'angry young men' who directed their anger impulsively outward in attacks on others, or inwardly toward themselves by overly self-destructive acts, or alternating between the two directions." Anectine was limited to extreme cases in which other forms of treatment had failed, the therapists insisted. A few of the men were given an injection immediately following an aggressive incident without any prior warning that they would receive such a treatment. Others were told in advance that they would be given an injection only if they committed certain acts. All the men, the therapists said, were told in advance the "nature" of the drug, although it is doubtful if the inmates were aware of its full effects.

Mattocks and Jew tried to set up what they called a "parent-child paradigm." They likened the therapy to situations in which a parent tries to make his children behave by telling them that they will be spanked if they do a certain thing again. "The use of the oxygen mask during treatment [to make sure the inmate would not stop breathing forever] was theorized to contribute to certain deep symbolic aspects related to the small child's feelings toward what he views as the omnipotent, beneficent parent figure who holds the power of life and death." But instead of mom and dad threatening to brandish with the back of their hands, the inmate under the influence of the drug was "counseled" by a doctor who described the act the man was being punished for over and over again. The doctor also admonished the inmate about how harmful the particular act was and told him that similar acts would result in similar treatments.

It all sounds straightforward and, from the standpoint of the men in white, it was. An inmate's perspective is another thing. In a recent novel called *Exile's End,* former Atascadero inmate Gary Livingston describes the experience. We pick up the story as the guards are handing out the nightly tranquilizers:

> "Amory!" Harrison hands a cup to a surly young black. . . .
> "Mancuso!" . . . No one comes.

"Say Frank, would you go find Harvey?"

Ranor walks up the hall. In a few moments Harvey's shouts echo, "I don't want any more of that shit!" . . .

"All right, let's not go through this again. Get him into seclusion." . . . "That's it, Harvey," Harrison says. "Remember what I told you last time. They're just going to have to give you Anectine again."

Harvey goes limp. "No Mr. Harrison, don't give me that."

"I'm sorry, Harv, but you don't give us much choice." . . .

And one morning soon they will take Harvey downstairs to an examining room, and strap him to the table. The doctors will drain Anectine from a vial while technicians wheel an oxygen tank closer. They will tell Harvey if he had behaved himself they wouldn't have to do this. The cotton ball will be cold on the tied vein, the needle inserted before he has time for a full breath or thought. Paralysis will sweep through him, pounding heart stilled, lungs unable to draw or burst, attempts at movement aborted. He will know he is dead as the doctor bends to softly warn, "Now, Harvey, you won't act up anymore, will you? It just doesn't pay. You know better than that . . ." And before unconsciousness, before a blurred hand reaches for the tank, he'll revive, tingling with frightened life, no wiser from knowing the next dose will be larger.

At Vacaville, Mattocks and Jew personally interviewed a little more than 50 percent of the inmates who underwent Anectine treatment. About half of the 35 men actually had received injections at the time the interviews were conducted. Despite the researchers' earlier assurance that only five of the men were entered into the program against their will, 18 men said they were enrolled involuntarily and another 11 said they signed up because their doctor asked them to. Only five men entered the program because they were seeking help. Although 54 percent of the inmates thought the doctors wanted to give them Anectine to help them, 37 percent thought it was for punishment. Describing their experience, 17 of the men said it was "scary or terrible," 13 said it was like dying, and 3 said it gave them a sensation of drowning. Only about half of the inmates thought the treatment was any help in controlling their behavior.

Somehow the researchers concluded that the program was a success, although they cautioned that the follow-up of just a few months was too short to be sure. They said that 61 percent of the subjects did not act out in one of the specified ways after getting into the program. There was also a 29.5 percent decrease in reported disciplinary infractions among the 15 men who received at least one injection, and a 22.9 percent decrease in the others.

At Atascadero, where the treatment originated, 90 inmates were reported to have received Anectine. Unlike Vacaville, where the injections were dependent on some specific inmate misbehavior, Atascadero inmates received a predetermined number of treatments. Three psychologists there (Martin J. Reimringer, Sterling W. Morgan and Paul F. Bramwell) described the scene in an issue of *Clinical Medicine*:

> After respiration stopped, the talking phase of the treatment began. Both negative and positive suggestions spoken in a confident, authoritarian manner were made by the male technician. The negative suggestions concerned the obliteration of unacceptable behaviors such as fighting and stealing. Positive suggestions focused upon the patient's becoming involved with patient government, taking individual responsibility, and increasing constructive socialization. These suggestions continued throughout the period of apnea [no breathing] and until the patient could verbally respond to the technician. After the treatment was completed, the patient was returned to his ward and no other special attention formally given to him.

The Atascadero therapists considered the program a success based on the frequency of "unacceptable" behavior following treatment. Some 68 percent of the inmates had no infractions for more than three months, 18 percent for from one to three months, and about 13 percent remained the same. But the results, like those at Vacaville, can be questioned on purely scientific terms, quite apart from any ethical considerations. There were no control groups at either institution to help measure whether it was the Anectine treatment itself that brought about any behavioral changes. Both institutions also included inmates with other problems (some mentally retarded or overtly psychotic) in the groups. Furthermore, there did not seem to be any master plan, especially at Vacaville, to determine who would get injections and when, and who would just be threatened with Anectine.

Atascadero bragged of its successes. For example, a sexual offender, who had 26 disciplinary infractions in two years for assaults and attempted suicides, received a series of Anectine treatments and was released within a year. Despite the figures, Atascadero was forced to end the program. A controversy arose following a visit to the institution by a law school student who complained to state authorities that the treatments were unethical. The Department of Mental Hygiene decided that the psychologists' preliminary report did not answer enough questions and did not really show that Anectine was more effective than a number of other, less offensive behavioral methods. The program was halted at Vacaville after 11 months because of lack of staff and an unwillingness of inmates to consent to treatment. "The prison grapevine works fast," said Dr. Arthur G. Nugent, chief psychiatrist, "and even the toughest have come to fear and hate the drug. I don't blame them—I wouldn't have the treatment myself for the world."

Atascadero continued for a while to try other kinds of aversion therapy, mainly electric shock aversion on homosexuals and child molesters. Some inmates were taught do-it-yourself aversion by snapping a rubber band against their wrists or sticking a finger down their throats any time unorthodox sexual thoughts started to intrude. When the late Dr.

Michael Serber, a respected behavior therapist himself, took over as clinical director of Atascadero following a staff shake-up in 1972, he banned the use of all aversive techniques. At that time he told a reporter for the *Advocate*, a nationwide homophile newspaper, "Mind you, I'm a behavior modifier and I don't have any qualms about using aversion therapy with a consenting adult who can walk out of my office and say, 'Screw you, I won't pay you.' But this kind of situation never applies at a state hospital and that's why I don't think aversion therapy should go on."

Dr. Serber made it clear that he thought the Anectine program was a prime example of prison bureaucracy run amuck. "They used it as punishment—and no one got busted for it," he mused. "I'm sort of shocked as an ethical psychiatrist to see that that kind of thing can get by. The ethics committee of the American Psychiatric Association investigated and didn't do a goddamn thing, which makes me very indignant." Several medical journals turned down a paper written by Dr. Serber and an associate criticizing the Anectine program. In another paper, describing a novel Atascadero program to train socially "inadequate" homosexuals to get along in a "regular" gay subculture, Dr. Serber revealed that harsh electroconvulsive therapy also was used as an aversive treatment. In reality, he said, it was "punishment for homosexual patients who had 'deviated' within the hospital."

Anectine has been used at least at one other California prison in recent years, the California Institute for Women at Frontera. There the subjects were women drug addicts. The drug supposedly increased their susceptibility to self-hypnosis and autosuggestion. Since officials at the facility considered the treatment experimental (unlike their counterparts at Vacaville and Atascadero), they filed a report on the program with the Food and Drug Administration. The FDA ordered the program halted for a while, but after an investigation, allowed it to continue. Officials at the prison said Anectine was successful in "significantly increasing susceptibility to autohypnosis."

There has been practically no outcry over the use of Anectine at the women's prison, and one of the reasons may be the detailed consent form which patients must read and sign. The women are told that Anectine is a "powerful drug" and that its use in a program to overcome drug addiction still is experimental. The form continues: "I further understand that succinylcholine administration in the manner described [inducing paralysis and a halt to breathing] may create considerable tension and apprehension, elevation in blood pressure and rapid heart beat during the period of action of the succinylcholine, as well as possible soreness of body muscles for a time after succinylcholine treatment."

•

The Iowa state prison system has been using the drug apomorphine in connection with a loosely organized aversion therapy program. The procedures have been carried out at the new Iowa Security Medical Facility at Oakdale, near Iowa City. The institution, which opened in 1968, is small (about 80 inmates) and costly, about $40 per inmate per day, compared with $12 a day at the older Iowa State Penitentiary at Fort Madison. The Iowa Security Medical Facility was built to handle court evaluations, "dangerous" inmates from mental hospitals, and mentally ill or "troublesome" prisoners from other state jails. The modern dormitory facilities are a novelty for many of the hardened criminals who have spent time in isolation cells at other Iowa prisons. Guidelines are made clear from the start: If you attack another inmate, we may restrain you in a chair; if you are aggressive and noisy, we might tape your mouth over. There is peer group and staff pressure, verbal warnings, brief stays in isolation, loss of cigarettes or meals, and the apomorphine.

It is an unusual kind of aversion program, to say the least, and seems much closer to outright punishment than to a conditioning therapy. The nausea-producing drug is administered by intramuscular injection after an inmate violates a behavioral code established for him by the staff. Punishable behavior can include not getting up, giving cigarettes against orders, talking, swearing, or lying. Frequently injections have been given based only on reports of other inmates (they used to call them "stoolies") without anyone on the staff personally observing the alleged violation and without specific authorization of a doctor.

When it is decided to administer the apomorphine, the inmate is taken to a small bathroom near the nurse's station and given the injection. He is exercised and in about 15 minutes he starts to vomit—something that lasts another 15 minutes to an hour. The staff of the security facility has claimed a 50- to 60-percent success rate in modifying unruly behavior through apomorphine. Until recently the treatment sometimes was started without the advance written consent of the inmate. If consent was given, the inmate could not change his mind and withdraw it.

In December 1973 a three-judge panel of the U.S. Circuit Court of Appeals for the Eighth Circuit, overruled a lower court and found the apomorphine program unconstitutional as it was then being administered. "Whether it is called 'aversive stimuli' or punishment, the act of forcing someone to vomit for a 15-minute period for committing some minor breach of the rules can only be regarded as cruel and unusual unless the treatment is being administered to a patient who knowingly and intelligently has consented to it," the judges ruled. They noted the testimony of a University of Iowa professor who called the treatment "really punishment worse than a controlled beating since the one administering the drug can't control it after it is administered." The judges added, "It is not possible to say that the use of apomorphine is a recognized and acceptable medical practice in institutions such as ISMF. Neither can we say, however, that its use on inmates who knowingly and intelligently consent to the treatment should be prohibited on a medical or a legal basis." They ordered the lower court to enjoin the state against further use of apomorphine except under a series of guidelines they laid out. These include advance written consent from the inmate who has been informed of the nature of the treatment in detail. The consent may be revoked at any time by the inmate. Each injection must be authorized individually by a doctor based only on personal observation by a staff member, not other inmates.

The less messy and more easily controlled electric shock treatment is the method preferred by other states. Wisconsin has had an electrical aversion therapy program, mainly for child molesters, since 1967. It is carried out at the Wisconsin Correctional Institution at Fox Lake, a modern, medium-security institution located between Madison and Green Bay.

On a voluntary basis inmates enter a small windowless cubicle and strap to one leg a leather color that is hooked up to a battery-powered shocker. Then they sit back and wait for the slide show to begin. As they punch a remote control button to change the slides, they might see a picture of a little girl on a merry-go-round. If they dawdle over that too long, they get an "uncomfortable" shock. The next slide will be a lusty redhead wearing a G-string and a beckoning look; there will not be any shock as long as that photo is left on the screen.

A similar program was started around the beginning of 1973 at the Connecticut Correctional Institution at Somers. In its first year and a half of operation, 9 of 15 habitual child molesters were paroled after being declared at least temporarily cured after 12 weeks of treatment. Officials are even more impressed with the results because they say that, traditionally, child molesters are loath to try any form of treatment, often out of fear that other prisoners will find out about the nature of their convictions. Pedophiles are the dregs of prison society and often are attacked and victimized by fellow prisoners. The fact that the aversion therapy is clear-cut and mechanical seems to appeal to the inmates, officials add. They say that the treatment is as voluntary as any can be in a prison setting.

Originally the program consisted solely of prisoners getting a shock on their inner thighs whenever provocative slides of naked children were flashed on the screen. The immediate effect is to knock out sexual fantasies about children. In an attempt to insure that this lasts, the inmates then are put under hypnosis and given covert sensitization. Before treatment starts, they supply a list of the things they fear the most—a dentist drilling, heights, insects—and the therapists make specialized tape recordings for each inmate associating these specific fears with sexual thoughts about children. Avoiding or leaving a sexually appealing encounter brings relief and pleasurable sensations, as do thoughts and pictures of adults.

One child molester at Somers, a 50-year-old skilled laborer who served a total of 16 years in prison since 1952 for child molesting, told the New York Times in May, 1974, "I used to have dreams and nightmares about the children I molested. Now I don't have them anymore. I couldn't have them if I tried. Children are not sexual objects to me anymore. I want to lead a normal life and go back to my wife and son. I'm tired of jail." The inmate admitted he had been skeptical and somewhat scared of the treatment in advance, but said it was not at all like he feared. "It doesn't hurt, but I hated it," he said.

The program received something of a blow when in early 1975, three of the imprisoned child molesters, joined by the American Civil Liberties Union, sued Somers in an attempt to stop the aversive shock program. The suit challenged the voluntariness of the project, claiming that prisoners are denied parole unless they participate.

Not all the aversion therapy programs in state prisons deal with allegedly violent or sexually disturbed inmates. Many prison psychologists use the treatment on the whole gamut of behavioral disorders that are treated in normal clinical settings. The State Prison of Southern Michigan, for example, treated a 21-year-old inmate who had suffered from stuttering since childhood. The therapists wanted to treat the man for his entire range of "problems in interpersonal relationships," but he insisted that his only real problem was stuttering and they agreed to help attack it. Twice a week for four months the inmate would go to the prison psychiatric clinic and read aloud three pages of a novel followed by about 15 minutes of small talk with the staff. For every five stutters he received an unpleasant shock. The therapists reported that the stuttering declined both in the clinic and in the cell block.

•

The controversial Patuxent Institution for Defective Delinquents in Jessup, Maryland, tried to use traditional aversion therapy but officials say they had to discontinue it because of heavy pressure. Such pressure has not stopped the Maryland facility, which can hold so-called defective delinquents indefinitely under state law, from using what it calls "negative reinforcement" techniques. A favorite involves a variation of the reward-and-punishment game in which an inmate is moved around, much like a Monopoly playing piece, into higher or lower "tiers" depending on how well he behaves and performs assigned tasks. Each higher graded tier offers a bit more freedom and other privileges. The punishment comes into play when the inmate moves backward for misbehaving. Patuxent also uses "sensory deprivation" which in prebehavior modification days used to be called "solitary confinement." One variation on the regular solitary confinement cell is an enclosed cubicle that is all white— walls, floor, furnishings, and so on. After a stay in one of these cells breaks down the old, aggressive personality, the behaviorists are ready to mold the inmate into an obedient, responsive citizen, or so they say. It sounds a little like army basic training.

Patuxent has suffered some recent court setbacks. In 1972 a two-judge panel held that inmates were being subjected to cruel and unusual punishment and ordered Patuxent to halt inhumane treatment "practiced in the name of therapy." In June 1973 another judge called the place "an odorous rat hole" and said the staff had to diagnose prisoners within six months or return them to regular prison.

But the biggest blow to Patuxent came when it was revealed that in its first 18 years the prison had spent more than $40 million and had released as cured only 12 percent of the men committed there. That caused a number of members of the Maryland General Assembly to propose a bill to abolish Patuxent.

Federal prisons have tried to stay out of the aversion therapy controversy. Norman A. Carlson, director of the Federal Bureau of Prisons, told a House of Representatives subcommittee in 1974: "For the record, let me state unequivocally that the Federal Bureau of Prisons has never used and does not countenance the use of psychosurgery, electroshock, sensory deprivation, massive use of psychoactive drugs, or any form of aversive treatment to change behavior, no matter how aggressive or resistive an offender may be to handle." Dr. Martin G. Groder, a psychiatrist who is warden of the new federal behavioral research center-cum-prison at Butner, North Carolina, was even stronger in promising he would not use any "methods of modern-day torture known as aversive conditioning, specifically the misuse of drugs, electric shock, or psychosurgery."

All of this rings a bit false to prisoners' groups and civil rights organizations. A group at the federal penitentiary at Marion, Illinois, sent a petition to the United Nations in July, 1972 charging that federal prisons use punishment and brainwashing techniques adapted from those used by the Communists during the Korean War. There was a brief "graded tier" type program at the federal prison at Springfield, Missouri. Called "START" (Special Treatment and Rehabilitative Training), it was plagued by controversy and poor results, and was stopped after 16 months. The government blamed high costs and "the small number of inmates who met the criteria developed for the program." START, the government insists in bureaucratic doubletalk, used only "positive rewards." Any slips by prisoners simply led to a removal of positive rewards, not punishment, officials claim.

Prisoners and groups that support them see in aversion therapy and other punishment techniques an attempt to suppress political dissent. "Psychological coercion is a very real weapon of prisoncrats," says Nick Di Soldo, an inmate at the Arizona state prison. "I have seen shock treatment—called 'Edison Medicine' by prisoners—used as punishment to reduce the vigor and vitality of jailhouse lawyers and inmates considered 'political radicals' by prison officials." The use and abuse of techniques developed by aversion therapists are worldwide problems. Amnesty International, a London-based organization that works for freedom for political prisoners, issued a report tracing newly developed techniques of torture to intensify pain without causing death as used in more than 30 countries to private and government-sponsored research starting in the 1950s. "Sensory deprivation," for example, has been employed against suspected members of the Irish Republican Army. As Dr. Timothy Shallice of London's National Hospital put it, "Torture, which was once a craft, has become a technology."

The Law Enforcement Assistance Administration, a U.S. government agency that dispenses federal anticrime funds to state and private agencies, announced in February 1974 that it was banning the use of such money for behavior modification research and programs. The decision was made, the agency said, mainly because it does not possess the technical and professional skills needed to screen, evaluate, or monitor projects dealing with such things as aversion therapy, chemotherapy, or psychosurgery. The statement failed to explain why the agency had suddenly recognized its inexpertise after five years of handing out grants totaling more than $600 million, a portion of which was funneled into behavior modification studies. Obviously the decision was a political one. Behavior modification had become a hot potato that caught the attention of the press and civil libertarian groups. Even Senator Sam Ervin's Subcommittee on Constitutional Rights had begun an investigation.

The Law Enforcement Assistance Administration decision did not really close the door on behavior modification. Numerous projects, including those dealing with aversion therapy, are still funded by the Department of Health, Education and Welfare, the Veterans Administration, other government and state agencies, and some private sources. An attempt by the author to get a handle on just how much in government funds is being spent on aversion projects was met by the typical Washington bureaucratic shuffle and exclamations of "Who, us?" If past attempts to gather government statistics are any indication, it is not that the officials are hiding the truth; they are ignorant of it. The latter explanation is perhaps even more frightening than the former one.

•

As noted in previous chapters, aversion therapy for people who break the law is not always confined to a prison setting. Suspended sentences or probation on the condition that the offender "seek help" are not unusual in cases of public drunkenness or commission of homosexual acts. British criminologist Neville Avison even suggested that people who commit serious traffic offenses be given electric shock aversion, the number of shocks to be determined in each case by the court with the level adjusted to the offender's "pain threshold." That does not seem too different from the state of Delaware where, until just a couple of years ago, a judge could sentence a felon to public whipping. In Delaware, at least, no pretense was made of whipping's "curative" powers.

One "seek-help" case involved a 48-year-old Welsh housewife, who was arrested 10 times for shoplifting and had served several sentences. She was put on probation on the condition that she seek treatment at the Morgannwg Hospital in Bridgend, Wales. Initial outpatient treatment with drugs and conventional psychotherapy seemed to work for a few years, but the woman committed another offense and was readmitted for electroconvulsive therapy to control her depression, and electrical aversion using imaginary scenes for the kleptomania. After 19 sessions she was discharged and treatment was continued on an outpatient basis. She stole again, was readmitted, and this time the electric shocks were given each time she took small personal possessions from a nearby table. This was abandoned after 11 sessions when the woman said the sessions were not really helping.

Alexander M. P. Kellam, her therapist, then decided to cast the housewife as the star in a very special film. Actually, a female psychologist, dressed in clothes similar to those of the housewife, was used as a stand-in. With the cooperation of a local store, the psychologist (the shots never showing her face) was filmed shoplifting various objects. "Extras" (nurses in training) were filmed with disapproving or disgusted looks on their faces. In the final film a shot of the housewife entering the hospital was used at the opening to make it seem as though she were the one doing the shoplifting. The 10-minute film showed 19 thefts, each followed by an onlooker showing surprise or disgust; it was at this time that electric shocks were given on a random basis.

After five weeks of treatment, during which the film was shown 40 times, the housewife reacted with anxiety every time a theft was shown whether or not a shock was given. This spread to a fear of all shops, and every time she entered one, she had a strong sensation of being watched. Three months later the woman reported she felt anxious on entering any store, but on five occasions she still had a strong urge to steal. At these times, she became very anxious, her left arm (the one to which the shocks were given) tensed, and the faces of the disapproving onlookers loomed large in her memory. She thought everyone in the store had turned to look at her, and the urge disappeared. The woman was shown the film four more times and arrangements were made to give booster showings every three months.

•

There has been widespread use of the punishment cure in numerous mental institutions and the psychiatric wards of community hospitals. While there have been recent moves in the direction of getting prior consent for the treatment from prisoners, such a matter is usually a moot point for a mental patient already out of touch with reality. Reported successes in this area also raise doubts about the claim of most aversion therapists that, in order for the punishment cure to work, it must be voluntarily accepted and fully understood by the client.

Sometimes mental patients have to wear "shock jackets," which are portable devices through which small shocks can be given by remote control whenever any prohibited behavior takes place. Thus the patients don't become antagonistic towards the therapist who is pressing the button. One psychiatrist who has used such devices, but isn't a fan of them, thinks they may help in a limited number of cases. "Let's face it," he says. "Aversive conditioning—under whatever name—is used all the time in mental wards all over the world. There are isolation rooms, restraints, group pressures and things like that. What I try to do is bring aversive consequences under some kind of control. I'm trying to remove the *atmosphere* of punishment mainly by setting up programs of positive reinforcement. Then, if unacceptable behavior occurs, or the patient doesn't exhibit the desired behavior, he doesn't get the reinforcement."

This psychiatrist feels that when aversive consequences are used, they should be reduced to the lowest possible level. For the therapy to work at all, he believes, approval of the patients is essential. "Otherwise it has as much effect as yelling at them," he adds. "And aversion conditioning alone is certainly no better than some other method. In addition, it's very necessary to establish a rapport with the patient, to reinforce an adaptive lifestyle with supportive psychotherapy. Aversion therapy can work to your disadvantage if the patient becomes fearful or angry at the therapist and avoids him and whatever else he is trying to do. Yet to rule out its use altogether could be seen as even worse punishment for a patient whom it might help."

Still, abuses seem to crop up more in mental hospitals than in other places, perhaps not so surprising when one considers how poorly paid and undertrained their staffs are. Outlandish disregard of the rules and of common sense led Minnesota to adopt stringent guidelines covering the use of almost all kinds of behavioral conditioning in state mental institutions. Similar problems were discussed a few years ago in an open and frank fashion at a seminar at California's Camarillo State Hospital. The main participants were Dr. Stanley Leiken, then staff psychiatrist at Camarillo's children's treatment center, and Dr. Thomas Ball, chief psychologist at Pacific State Hospital near Pomona, California. Dr. Leiken told of Bobby, a very destructive child who was constantly tearing up anything and everything in sight. "We got new furniture; Bobby tore the furniture. If we got books and play materials, Bobby would tear them." Finally Dr. Leiken decided to set up a rigid program of punishment under which he was alerted every time Bobby acted destructively. "He and I would go into the punishment room and for each bit of material he tore, I would slap him fiercely on the hands [along] with angry words. This was not difficult to do because I was very angry and it was in an organized kind of way. Well, I began to find out that at the same time there began to be all kinds of slapping of other kids in the cottage.

"It seems as if it was during this time that it began," Dr. Leiken said. "Before that time there was a general rule that you don't hit kids. I think that my doing this, even in an organized way, sort of gave them [the staff members] permission to do it in a disorganized way. It certainly is not what we should like to have. It is not the carefully planned-out aversive techniques to deal with or to modify specific behavior. It is giving license to the staff to deal with feelings that they have had a hell of a time dealing with anyway, and somehow I gave them permission to deal with them now. . . . I feel that the kind of thing I did might have been of value to Bobby, but it may have been a real disservice to the rest of the cottage and the staff. . . . There is this basic fear that it [aversion therapy] won't be used in a therapeutic way. In state hospitals we know that we do not have control over many of our staff."

Someone in the audience suggested that spanking would always be a good form of punishment, but Dr. Leiken responded with the case of Sharon, a child who frequently threw violent tantrums. "She is the kind of girl who elicits the most intense feeling of any child in the cottage, and yet she is the child for whom this kind of technique would be the most contraindicated. She has had it ever since day one; she has been beaten black and blue by everyone who has come in contact with her, and it is not going to work. It has not been done in any kind of a way that has been helpful." Instead, the most effective aversive treatment for Sharon, who craves and requires human contact, would be total isolation, Dr. Leiken said.

Dr. Ball warned that aversion therapy could become the easy answer at hospitals. "It can become a shortcut for thinking," he said. "We might devise techniques of positive reinforcement to deal with some of these problems, but if we had the shock stick available and right there on hand, we would get it and use it. . . . There are specific cases where punishment is justified. Yet you have to carefully consider its ramifications in terms of possible patient abuse. . . . We certainly have to keep it under scrutiny."

What some professional may see as the legitimate use on children of a technique they call "aversion therapy" is sometimes viewed by others as outright punishment or torture. Examples abound. An award-winning NBC television documentary, "This Child Is Rated X," took a look at the Elgin State Mental Hospital in a Chicago suburb, which has a special unit to deal with youngsters who get caught in the web of Cook County Juvenile Court. The children are called "socially deprived," not "mentally ill" or "emotionally disturbed." Legal Aid attorney Patrick Murphy told producer Martin Carr about two 13-year-old boys at Elgin State who were caught engaging in consensual homosexual conduct and were tied, spread-eagled, to their beds for 77½ hours; they were allowed up only to shower. They also received painful intramuscular injections of an unspecified drug, and were put on display in the middle of a dormitory room.

When questioned, Dr. Enrique Vicioso, then clinical director of the hospital's adolescent division, told Carr: "We're not using punishment over here. We are using a multiplicity of treatment in order to change the behavior of the person. . . . We are trying to provide here in this institution, to some of the kids, some kind of therapeutical behavior modification and some kind of disciplinary approach to the patient." The drugs were given intramuscularly, "because we want the medication to work as fast as possible so the behavior can be modified," Dr. Vicioso said. A young girl at the hospital was tied to her bed for seven consecutive days for slapping a matron, but again Dr. Vicioso insisted that was not punishment, but therapy. "Everybody tried to really help this girl to modify that behavior, but unfortunately . . . [she] has not been kept . . . in a place long enough so she may be able to learn about that," he added.

In the summer of 1974 the U.S. Senate Permanent Subcommittee on Investigations heard testimony from government investigators about a private school in Florida for emotionally disturbed and delinquent children. The school superintendent called the methods he used behavior modification techniques but Senator Henry Jackson said they reminded him of the Nazi concentration camp at Buchenwald. They included using bull whips, rusty handcuffs and leg irons, and leather collars with wires attached to an electric shock generator. The shock machine itself was lovingly called the "Lalapalooza." Senate investigators said similar schools

are springing up all over the country. Although they call
themselves psychiatric hospitals or residential psychiatric
treatment centers, the investigators had another name: commercially operated jails.

•

Many of the 2,000 patients at the Bien Hoa Mental Hospital in South Vietnam saw aversion therapy firsthand in 1967.
Dr. Lloyd H. Cotter, a California psychiatrist, went to Bien
Hoa for a few months as part of the U.S. wartime assistance
program. He decided to introduce what he calls "operant conditioning" for patients in the chronic wards, most of whom
were diagnosed as schizophrenics. The hospital was overcrowded, understaffed, and short on food so Dr. Cotter decided on a mass treatment approach.

"We started the program on a ward of 130 male patients
by announcing that we were interested in discharging patients to make the hospital less crowded," he says. "Who
wanted to go home? About 30 patients indicated their interest." The patients were told they had to work first for three
months to prove they would not be a burden at home; 10
agreed and the rest refused. "To all the remaining patients we
announced, 'People who are too sick to work need treatment.
Treatment starts tomorrow—electroconvulsive treatment. It is
not painful and is nothing to be afraid of. When you are well
enough to work, let us know." Perhaps electroconvulsive therapy (ECT) is not painful, but the direct shocks to the brain
cause convulsions and blackouts. Also, because the hospital
was low on drugs, none of the 120 men who received treatment the next day were given an injection of succinylcholine
to ward off any possible bone fractures—an illegal procedure
in many countries. (No fractures were reported, "perhaps because of the smaller size and musculature of the Vietnamese
people," Dr. Cotter reports.) The electroconvulsive therapy
continued three times a week and more and more patients
started working.

The treatment was not as successful on a women's ward.
After a series of 20 shocks, only 15 of 130 women were work-

ing, so Dr. Cotter came up with another aversive technique: starvation. "After three days without food," he says, "all the remaining patients volunteered to work." Dr. Cotter and his Vietnamese associates were kept busy administering thousands of shocks as they went from ward to ward but the psychiatrist says he was troubled by another problem. How could they discharge those patients who had completed their three-month work period, but who did not have a responsible relative to whom they could be released? By happy coincidence, Dr. Cotter says, he heard that the Green Berets needed agricultural teams to grow and harvest crops at their A-camps, which were forts in Viet Cong-occupied territory, right in the middle of some of the bloodiest fighting of the war. Not only would the ex-mental patients be paid, but they could be "incorporated into the life of the camp and made to feel that they were important members of the team," Dr. Cotter adds.

To answer any criticism that his methods were cruel, the psychiatrist draws a rather shaky analogy between electroconvulsive therapy or starvation and giving a child with pneumonia an antibiotic injection. "The injections hurt and even involve some slight risk to the patient, but the damage without their use is potentially much greater," he says. "Inflicting a little discomfort to provide motivation to move patients out of their zombielike states of inactivity, apathy, and withdrawal was, in our opinion, well justified." No one, however, asked the patients, although Dr. Cotter says that when he walked through the fields, "I was not struck or threatened."

Electroconvulsive therapy was originated by two Italians in 1938 after they saw pigs go into convulsions when they were shocked prior to being slaughtered. Traditionally it has been used to treat schizophrenia and depression, based primarily on an old observation that symptoms of some mental patients may disappear following spontaneous convulsions. Its use in aversive conditioning is rare, but besides the Vietnamese case, at least one group of American researchers have tried it, although they shy away from calling it aversion therapy. Their technique is to have patients with obsessive or compulsive feelings act those feelings out. When symptoms of agitation become observable, the patients are injected with

Anectine (to reduce the risk of fracture) and when muscle twitching starts they receive a large jolt to the head which causes convulsions and blackout. The researchers, who include the head of the psychology clinic at Rutgers University, say that following a single session of electroconvulsive therapy all of their patients showed dramatic improvement for periods ranging from three months to three years. The success, they feel, is due to the amnesiac properties of the shocks but other researchers see it more along the lines of a punishment cure.

•

Other kinds of shock treatment have greater acceptance in most mental institutions. A particular favorite seems to be the electric cattle prod, especially the Sabre-Six model manufactured by Hot Shot Products Company. The prod, which saw some action during civil rights demonstrations in the mid-1960s, often is used to control and treat violent behavior. At the Mendota State Hospital in Madison, Wisconsin, the prod was used on a 31-year-old woman who had been hospitalized for about nine years and diagnosed as a chronic paranoid schizophrenic. Doctors decided to eliminate three kinds of behavior: aggressive acts, verbal threats, and accusations of being persecuted and abused. The shock was administered as soon as possible after the behavior, and immediately preceding it a staff member would tongue-lash the patient ("no hitting," "no threats") so she would know why she was being punished.

Each time the woman was jolted, she would let out a cry, stiffen all over, and begin whimpering. She also exclaimed such things as, "The only thing holding me back is the faradic stimulator," and "If it wasn't for the faradic shock, you'd be on your ass." The behaviors were not completely eliminated and there were occasional flare-ups while the treatment program continued. But the woman began to be more responsive to social reinforcement and her paranoia decreased. A little more than two years later she was released to live on her own.

A similar method was tried with Carol, a 24-year-old moderately retarded and seriously violent patient at the University of Kentucky Medical Center. She previously had received 20 electroconvulsive therapy sessions, but became progressively more violent. The prod was introduced and she was told, "If you hit other people, you will be punished." Staff members alternately provoked her and gave positive social reinforcement for appropriate behavior. Step by step she was taken from her isolated cubicle back into the regular ward activities, all the time receiving shocks for assaultive behavior. The therapists reported a "dramatic change" in frequency of assaults. In a one-year period following treatment, there were only four aggressive incidents. Unfortunately, one of the incidents was so violent and unpredicted that the female staff became extremely fearful of Carol, and she now is locked in seclusion and allowed out only a few hours a day in the company of a male aide. The aversion therapy program was discontinued, mainly because of staff fear, the therapists say. "It is still an open question as to what the results might have been if the program had been instituted earlier in her life," they add.

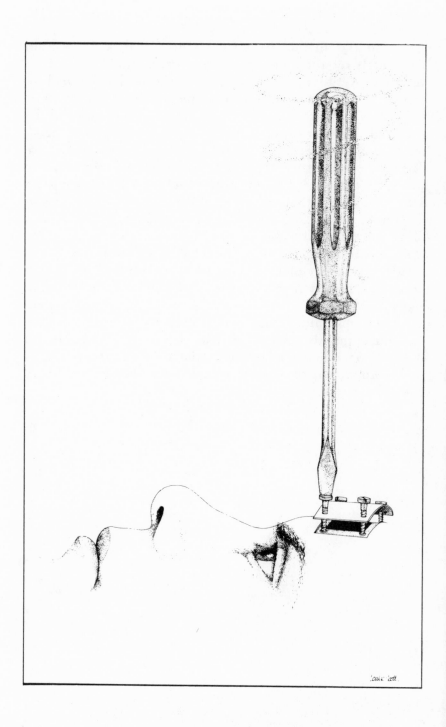

Chapter IX

FUTURE SHOCK?

"God, Priscilla, I can't remember a quieter Friday night in Sector 57 in months, maybe a year," the young technician says as she scans the large map display of a 100-square-block area of south-central Los Angeles.

"I know, Pam. Even central control has had only a half dozen code yellows for the whole city in the last couple of hours." Priscilla glances again at her computer display screen. Normal location checks of the sector's 138 resident parolees flash by in seconds.

The door to the sector room silently slides open. "Look busy," Pam whispers. "This is that tour group of German police officers. Hey, subdirector Carberry himself is leading it!"

"Good evening ladies," the subdirector says. "I trust things have been as quiet here as in the rest of the sector rooms tonight? Good, good. Now if you gentlemen will step behind the monitor desk there, I'll explain what we do in a sector room." The Germans crowd behind the long console filled with electronic equipment and display screens.

"Now we've already shown you how we either implant the transmitter-stimulator units directly under the skin of the parolee or attach it to a wrist or ankle band that will automatically signal us if the subject tries to take it off. The units themselves aren't that powerful, so we have thousands of receivers strategically placed all over the area to pick up their signals and transmit them here to central control."

One of the Germans interrupts. "Mr. Subdirector, what kind of opposition did you have from the civil rights groups when this program was first suggested?" he asks.

"Oh, they bitched and whined at first—and they're still not too happy with it. But you've got to remember, the choice is still up to the convict. He can stay in prison if he wants. Or he can take his aversion therapy and agree to wear the monitor when we release him into the community. Anytime he wants out of the program, he's always welcome back to the comfort of jail." The subdirector flashes a wan smile and continues.

"Now this sector room, like all the others, is primarily responsible for monitoring—and if necessary, stimulating— the parolees who live within sector boundaries. Those moving blips of light on the map let us keep constant tabs on the whereabouts of Sector 57's parolees and any others who wander in from outside the sector. We usually dispatch a squad car to check on the outsiders and see what they're up to. Never hurts to show the flag, you know."

"But how do you keep track of the individuals? How do you know where?. . ."

"Well, Herr Superintendent, if you'd permit me, I was just getting to that. That's where TASS comes in. That's for 'Tracking and Stimulating System,' our super computer which has complete information on every parolee plus data about the makeup of the city. So when . . . uh, Ms. Hawley, I believe that while you've been staring at me, your screen has gone from a code yellow to a flashing code orange."

"Oh Christ," Pam mutters under her breath, whirling around to face the display. "Priscilla punch up case BMF-547."

"Brown, Marc F. Age 32. Alcohol-induced aggression. Charge: assault and battery with a knife. Sentence: one to two years. Aversively conditioned, shock and nausea, 24 sessions. Released three months ago. No prior flare-up."

One of the white light blips on the map has turned orange

and seems to be doing a jig. "Ms. Hawley, could that be a tavern that our friend Mr. Brown is pacing in front of?" the subdirector asks.

"Let's see," the technician says, punching the location into the computer. "Yes sir, it sure is. And the biomedical monitor indicates the subject's heartbeat has quickened measurably and the anxiety indicator . . . whoops, there he goes inside. I'd better punch this up to central control before we have a code red."

"Now gentlemen, you're seeing some action," the subdirector says. "A code red would indicate that the internal body sensors have detected alcohol in the bloodstream. In that case we'd have to send a patrol car out and physically pick up Mr., uh, whatever his name is. With a code orange, however, central control will administer a 'booster' electric shock. That's usually enough in 90 percent of the cases. . . . Yes, look, the blip is retreating, picking up speed. Now it's turned back to yellow. If the biomedical signs calm down within five minutes, it'll become white again."

"Excuse me," another German asks, "but couldn't you just have the computer administer the shock directly?"

"Oh, sure, technically yes," the subdirector says. "But we still want to retain some human control over the system. The shock can only be administered by the psychology duty officer. There may be some cases where you'd want to delay the shock or see if the situation itself is aversive enough to make the parolee leave. We frequently give homosexuals up to five minutes exposure in a gay bar before we stimulate them."

"Stimulate?" asks a German.

"Shock if you prefer. By any name it almost always sends them running."

"But isn't that a bit, well . . ."

"Barbaric? Inhumane? Look, these people are all volunteers. We're not punishing them; we're just conditioning them to help them get rid of an undesirable behavior. No one's twisting their arms."

"But what about the overall success rate? I mean does all this really work? Do you keep them from repeating?"

"Umm . . . yes . . . Time to move on, gentlemen. I'm sure

you'll find central control a fascinating place. The level of sophistication. . . ."

•

1984? Perhaps, or maybe a lot sooner. Although the preceding is a fantasy, everything in it is based on present-day technology and detailed suggestions that have appeared in medical and legal journals in the past few years. In fact, a prototype of just such a system has already been field tested. Psychotechnology is expanding in other directions. Doctors now implant electrodes directly in the brain, leaving them there for years at a time. The electrodes are used to stimulate the brain's pain or pleasure centers and are capable of producing the most intense orgiastic joys—or intractable agony, aggression, and depression. At the same time, aversion therapy is expanding rapidly into new areas and becoming easier to use. This makes it essential that the legal and ethical aspects of the punishment cure receive a full public hearing.

Two social scientists who have written extensively about what they call an electronic rehabilitation system for parolees are Ralph K. Schwitzgebel, a lecturer in psychology at Harvard Medical School, and his twin brother Robert L., who teaches psychology at Claremont Graduate School in California. Ralph Schwitzgebel and associates have developed a prototype system consisting of two small units (a transmitter and battery pack), each about the size of a thick paperback book and weighing around 2 pounds. The range of the prototype covers only the interior of one large building plus a five- or six-block area around it. As the wearer walks through a monitored area, strategically placed repeater stations pick up a subject's coded signal and transmit it to a base station where it is observed and recorded. A modified missile tracking device plots the wearer's location and flashes it on a screen. The base station can send signals back to the wearer. These could trigger anything from a loud noise from a hidden ear speaker to an electric shock. Equipment is also available that could sound an alarm automatically if someone tries to remove or disable his electronic leech.

Ralph Schwitzgebel says the main purpose of the prototype is to see if a larger and more complex system would be feasible. Through the use of repeater stations, much like the microwave system used for television transmission, the monitor system could theoretically cover large areas. It would be capable of 24-hours-a-day monitoring and really wouldn't be much more complex than those now used by police departments or transit companies to keep track of their vehicles. In addition to monitoring a person's location, the device could also monitor voice, blood pressure, heartbeat, and other physiological activity. For instance, the monitor could be hooked up to a device to measure penile erections so that it could keep a very close watch on sex offenders in the community, Schwitzgebel adds in a pamphlet published by the National Institute of Mental Health. Robert Schwitzgebel suggests that verbal behavior could be monitored by the devices and regulated by a central computer. When, for example, the frequency of hostile statements per hour exceeded a certain predetermined limit, the subject could be beeped or shocked automatically.

Ralph Schwitzgebel says that all the components of a "very powerful, involuntary surveillance system" have now been developed. His group has used the system on volunteers. Sixteen subjects, ranging from a young businessman with no criminal record to a man with more than 100 arrests and eight years in jail, wore prototype surveillance units. Since the range was limited, they had to agree to stay within a block of their homes, jobs, schools or watering holes. Within five days, two thirds of the men dropped out of the research project, and most of the rest were gone by the end of 15 days. One subject however, wore his bug for five months. Schwitzgebel says that extensive psychological tests did not show any marked negative changes in the subjects. He does note, however, that some of them simply removed the equipment prior to a "forbidden" bout of drinking or sexual promiscuity.

The Harvard lecturer reports more success with a man who had a history of aggression following heavy drinking. The subject had received aversion therapy and was conditioned to become nauseous when he was served alcohol. This was always preceded by a particular tone signal (much like Pavlov's bell). Later, the tone signal was transmitted to the subject by remote control whenever he entered taverns in high crime districts.

The assumption is that an electronic parole system could suppress unwanted behavior more effectively by using mild punishment for each misstep rather than occasionally using harsh punishment, Robert Schwitzgebel says. His brother foresees the day when prisons might no longer be necessary if misbehavior either can be predicted in advance or well regulated within the setting of the community. If a prisoner believes that the electronic equipment infringes on his rights and freedom, he can simply return to jail and serve out his sentence, Ralph Schwitzgebel adds.

The psychologist concedes that a highly developed system could lead to abuses and calls on his fellow social scientists to begin considering procedures to regulate its use. He warns that there could be temptations to use such a system on patients with suicidal tendencies, mentally ill or retarded people, patients with a history of heart trouble and even government employees with highly sensitive jobs. Among the safeguards suggested to stop the use of the bugs on nonprisoners is development of a legal right-to-privacy doctrine or invoking the Fifth Amendment privilege against self-incrimination. For parolees, monitoring might be permitted only if long-term therapeutic benefits could be proven; installation still might need the approval of an independent civil libertarian group. Schwitzgebel has said that "legal coercion" might sometimes be required to get offenders to take part in a monitoring program, but says that in the long run their rights might be more protected by continual bugging than by present parolee inspection techniques. In the end, it should always be up to the prisoner himself to make the decision, he adds. But who would see to it that there were no flagrant abuses in the program? The same people who plant the bugs, of course. By having psychologists or their professional organizations set up the ground rules, there would be more "flexibility and conceptual integrity," Schwitzgebel says. Legislators and judges could then use these professional standards to help them solve really difficult problems, he adds. Big Brother, then, may not be a politician after all. He may be the guy down the street with a Ph.D. in psychology.

•

Joan P., an attractive and charming 20-year-old girl with a history of epileptic seizures, certainly did not look violent as she sat in the small lab strumming her guitar. But her doctors knew that she frequently flew into violent and unpredictable rages that occasionally led to physical assaults. She already had stabbed a stranger with a knife and twisted a scissors blade into a nurse's chest. For the moment though, all was calm. Then Dr. José M. R. Delgado fiddled with some switches. Within seven seconds Joan flung her guitar away, became enraged, and started throwing herself against the wall. She then paced around the room for several minutes before gradually calming down and becoming cheerful again.

Joan had not suffered another of her spontaneous attacks. This one was man made, courtesy of Dr. Delgado and the electrodes he had implanted deep inside Joan's brain. Dr. Delgado, formerly at Yale and now at the University of Madrid Medical School, is one of the developers of a new technique called "electronic stimulation of the brain," or ESB. Already hundreds of men and women have had up to a dozen or more needle-thin electrode wires placed in their brains for up to several years. The electrode implanting often is a prelude to surgical destruction or removal of part of the brain in an attempt to control a physical ailment or problem behavior. In Joan's case, for example, the tiny electrical impulse that set off the girl's aggressive behavior also helped Dr. Delgado pinpoint a target area in her brain as the site for a destructive lesion.

Another pioneer, Dr. Robert G. Heath, head of the Department of Psychiatry and Neurology at Tulane University School of Medicine, has implanted electrodes in more than 65 patients over the past 25 years. Dr. Heath concentrates on a particular site, the septal region, which seems to be the brain's "pleasure center." In one case the doctor "conditioned" a

24-year-old homosexual (also diagnosed as epileptic) into having his first heterosexual intercourse. The man was given a
device to control his own electrodes. He repeatedly pressed
only the button that sent electronic impulses to the septal
region. He was given the device for three-hour sessions and
he stimulated himself up to 1,500 times in that period. The
patient then reported feelings of pleasure, alertness, warmth,
and sexual arousal with a compulsion to masturbate. Always
willing to help, Dr. Heath provided the man with heterosexual stag films (which he had previously spurned) and gave him
a private cubicle in which to do his thing. During the next
week, sex was always on the young man's mind, and again the
obliging Dr. Heath helped out. This time he provided a young
female prostitute and an extension cord for the man's electrodes "to give him adequate mobility." The result, says Dr.
Heath, was "highly satisfactory."

Dr. Delgado's patients are always mobile since the implanted "stimoceivers," which simultaneously monitor data
from the brain and provide stimulation, operate with FM radio waves. If the electrodes are implanted in the proper spots,
then electronic impulses can block the thinking process, in-
hibit speech and movement, or bring on pleasure, laughter,
friendliness, gabbiness, hostility, fear, hallucinations, and
memories, Dr. Delgado says. The effects are startling. Pulses
to one patient's brain, for instance, forced the man to make a
fist, despite a request from the doctor that he try to resist. "I
guess, doctor, that your electricity is stronger than my will,"
the patient said. An 11-year-old boy under stimulation voiced
a thinly veiled wish to marry the male interviewer and later
said, "I'd like to be a girl."

Dr. Delgado has stopped charging bulls in midflight and
"overthrown" the bosses of monkey colonies with electronic
stimulation of the brain. He suggests that the same techniques
someday could be used to stop soldiers from firing guns, or
politicians and generals from giving them the orders to do so.
On the other hand Dr. Delgado says that traditional methods
of reward and punishment would be more effective in changing behavior than implanted electrodes. The complexity of
ESB procedures act as a safeguard against their improper use
by untrained or unethical persons, he adds.

Some researchers think that Dr. Delgado's electrode implants and the electronic parole system of the Brothers Schwitzgebel would make perfect marriage partners and lead to the ultimate in aversion therapy. Two criminologists, Barton L. Ingraham and Gerald W. Smith, glory in the new technology that "will soon make possible the observation and control of human behavior without actual physical contact." Writing in *Issues in Criminology,* they note that ESB tied in with a vast computer network could be used either for direct conditioning by manipulating rewards and punishments, or by blocking "criminal" responses. The latter could be accomplished by electronically producing fear, anxiety, disorientation, loss of memory, or even loss of consciousness. The criminologists are somewhat cautious. "None of the research indicates that man's every action can be directed by a puppeteer at an electrical keyboard," they say. "None indicates that thoughts can be placed into the heads of men electrically; none indicates that man can be directed like a mechanical robot. *At most,* they indicate that some of man's activities can possibly be deterred by such methods. . . . "

With their conditional "at most" on the books, Ingraham and Smith go on to describe a system in which an implanted monitoring device sends back to a computer detailed physiological data on a parolee, such as respiration, muscle tension, and presence of adrenalin in the bloodstream. If this is read along with the ex-con's location (a former burglar is breathing hot and heavy in the downtown shopping district at midnight), "it would be a safe guess . . . that he was up to no good," the criminologists say. The computer would weigh the probabilities and either alert the police or parole officer to hasten to the scene or send a not so polite "message" to one of the subject's brain implants. In the long run, the authors suggest, this would be a lot cheaper and safer for society as a whole than the present-day prison system.

Subliminally zapping a paroled offender every time he makes a suspicious move might cut the crime rate, but does it rehabilitate the man? Or is it turning him into a nonmoral agent—a clockwork orange—who cannot be praised or damned for his conduct? These are among the questions raised by Michael H. Shapiro, an associate professor at the

University of Southern California Law Center. Who would be offered the implanted electrodes? Just the convicted burglar serving a five-year term, or a rapist in for life? Would they be offered to white-collar criminals, the forgers and embezzlers? Shapiro is vehemently opposed to such a system being used by anyone. "A system in which a person's acts . . . are in fact *not his own* but those of *another* is one in which he is not free in any legal or moral sense," Shapiro says. "He is under the dominion of another. . . . This condition . . . is suspect both constitutionally and morally."

•

Regardless of whether the visions of future shock become reality, aversion therapy still raises the hackles of critics, especially when it is used on inmates in prisons or mental institutions. "The dividing line between aversion therapy and old-fashioned torture can become very thin and disappear altogether," says Edward M. Opton, Jr., senior research psychologist and an associate dean of the Wright Institute, a graduate school of psychology in Berkeley, California. "The classic example is the use of Anectine in the California prisons," he adds.

One of Opton's prime concerns is the misuse of medical and psychological terminology for political or punitive purposes. In a letter to the author, he gives an example.

Amputation is a lifesaving medical treatment. If I had gangrene in my hand, I would certainly want to have it amputated. But cutting off a robber's hand, as is done today in Libya and as used to be done in western countries, is punishment.

Now if such a punishment were forbidden by law, administrators could translate it into medical treatment: "We prescribe surgical removal of the digital extremity, as this is the organ that has demonstrated pathological behavior, and excision of this pathological tissue has been shown to have 100 percent effectiveness in preventing recurrence of the behavioral

aberration." Since prisoners have no legal right (unfortunately) to refuse medical treatment, prison authorities could thus evade the judgment of the
legislature and of the judiciary that mutilation shall
no longer be performed.

Of course, such nonsense would be far too obvious. The prison authorities could not get away with
it, and so they probably would never even think of it.
What makes some of the new technologies [such as]
aversion therapy . . . attractive to certain politicians
and prison administrators, is that they can carry out
the translation of punishment into medical terminology without acknowledging it to anyone—probably
without even confronting it in their own consciences.

One of the big problems with the use of aversion therapy
in prisons and mental institutions is the issue of informed
consent. Since California's aborted romance with the
"clockwork orange cure," almost everyone gives at least lip
service to the idea that aversion therapy should not be used
without an inmate's completely voluntary and thoroughly informed consent. Many argue, however, that such consent is
really impossible because of the "inherently coercive" institutional atmosphere. A former inmate of California's Atascadero
State Hospital says that informed consent is a joke. "The victims [inmates about to receive a treatment] are baited with
early release, special privileges, a hall card—small things,
some of them, but not when you're at Atascadero," he adds.

Constitutional lawyer Ephraim Margolin has looked into
the controversy. "Consent obtained by bribery would not
hold up in a court of law," he says. "Besides, the prisoner
can't appreciate the possible side effects. Most prisoners have
no scientific training. How much can they understand of what
is being done to them?" Bolstering that view, a three-judge
state court in Michigan ruled in 1973, in a case involving
psychosurgery, that an involuntarily confined mental patient
cannot really give his legitimate consent because he is living
in "an inherently coercive atmosphere" that deprives him of
any real choices because of the pressure it imposes on him.

Completely outlawing the use of aversion therapy on confined individuals may go too far in the opposite direction. The warden at one California prison was widely quoted as saying of his charges who did not want certain treatments, "If they want to stay cuckoo and stay locked up all their lives, that's all right with us." Of course that is a coercive and threatening statement, but everything about prison and most mental institutions is coercive and threatening. If a form of treatment is the only chance an inmate has of getting out of that setting, should not that option be open for him? The question, then, would be how to make consent as informed and noncoercive as possible given the situation.

Congress passed a law in 1974 setting up a fact-finding National Commission for the Protection of Human Subjects of Biomedical and Behavioral Research. The law also sets up institutional review boards at all facilities receiving government research grants. The boards, among other things, are to see to it that informed consent means just that. Congress defined informed consent as meaning the consent of a person or his legal representative given as a matter of free choice "without the intervention of any elements of force, fraud, deceit, duress, or other form of constraint or coercion." The law also lists the types of advance information that a subject must be supplied including possible risks and benefits of a treatment and any appropriate alternative procedures that might be available. Bills also have been introduced in at least two states, California and Arizona, which would prohibit almost entirely the use of aversion therapy on inmates without their prior informed consent. Both bills would require a court order to administer the therapy to inmates who refused to give consent or who lacked the capacity to make an informed decision.

•

Some behavior therapists insist that they do not need any outside help in deciding when to use aversive techniques. Halmuth H. Schaefer, a California psychologist now teaching at the University of Auckland in New Zealand, takes the suggestion of outside review and intervention as a personal and professional affront. "Only a country that has the lowest regard for her scientists can impose such a stipulation," he says. "Only a public that has been conditioned through a steady diet of Frankensteins and other mad movie scientists can seriously believe that such controls are necessary." Schaefer thinks that if a therapist believes a certain treatment, no matter how nasty, will work for a client, it is ethical to use it. He does admit that there were some "almost unbelievable abuses" in the name of human experimentation in German prison camps during World War II, "but the question is whether these abuses could have been prevented by reviews of laymen or peers who are less informed" than the therapist. Schaefer answers his own rather naive question by saying that "the professional's conscience must be his own as well as the public's guide." Further, he exhorts superintendents of institutions, governors, and even the president not to "simply worry about being embarrassed by what the scientists under his administration do, but . . . prepare the public to tolerate what these scientists do."

Contrast that with what law professor Michael Shapiro has to say about the Atascadero and Vacaville Anectine "treatment" programs in California: "These gross episodes of assaults upon personal autonomy should dispatch any notions that officialdom in general or the medical profession in particular can safely be left to their own devices in determining the nature of, and occasion for, intervention in human mentation for purposes of achieving mind/behavior control." Shapiro calls for quick legislative and judicial action to control the use of behavior modification. He realizes that outright prohibition or overly stringent controls would lead to a "Catch-22" situation: "You may use any therapy you wish, as long as it doesn't work; if it works, it is forbidden." There's a clear need to balance a right to treatment with a right to remain free from governmental limitations on personal liberty. Treatment that is not given in one case may destroy human liberty and potential as much as enforced treatment in another case, Shapiro adds. The professor weighs the alternatives and comes down on the side of permitting aversive conditioning after truly informed consent by inmates, despite the coercive atmosphere in institutions. "I don't think that anyone, state or individual, has the moral standing to substitute his judgment for that of the competent inmate," he concludes.

Dr. Seymour L. Halleck, of the department of psychiatry of the Medical School of the University of North Carolina, Chapel Hill, has another possible solution. He is concerned because a method such as aversion therapy can work so quickly that a patient is not likely to think about the meaning of his behavior or consider the social consequences of his treatment. Dr. Halleck suggests that aversive treatments for nonconsenting inmates or those who consent under duress only be used if the person's behavior imminently threatens the physical well-being of himself or others. Such a decision would have to be reviewed in advance and would require the approval of a monitoring board consisting of the therapist who recommended the treatment, an outside psychiatrist, and an attorney.

In an essay in the *American Journal of Psychiatry*, Dr. Halleck sounds completely opposed to aversion therapy and, indeed, in an interview he says, "I think that 95 percent of the time it's not justified and should be banned." But the psychiatrist also admits that he headed a staff of therapists in the Wisconsin state prison system when aversion therapy was instituted for sex offenders. "There are times when—with informed consent—I've used it and found it can be helpful," Dr. Halleck says. "We had these sex offenders and had put them through 50 different kinds of treatment and they weren't changing. These guys were all on indeterminate sentences and they just couldn't get out without showing some signs of change. One of my staff asked me if I wanted to try aversion therapy, and I found it incredibly benign. And the patient himself helps you find a painful enough level of shock." Then does he favor aversion therapy? "No, no, but these guys knew the ins and outs of informed consent. Look, I didn't make the law that stuck them there, and this was one way—a gimmick, perhaps—that we saw to get them out. And the treatment was helpful in convincing the parole board that they were better and some of them were released. I assume they're doing okay."

Dr. Halleck believes that worse abuses of aversive and

other behavior modification treatments could take place with truly voluntary patients outside of institutions. "The problem is that while alleviation of suffering through treatment may serve the patient's short-term needs, the behavioral changes produced by treatment may not serve the patient's long-term needs and eventually be of more value to those around him than to the patient himself," he says. "To the extent that we treat and extinguish behaviors that are designed to influence the environment that is bothering the patient, we tend to preserve the stability of the social system and risk becoming agents of the status quo." Efforts must be made, he adds, to increase a patient's awareness of his social situation and thus the real reasons he is seeking treatment and what the outcome might be.

•

Perry London probably has spent as much time as anyone pondering and writing about the future of behavior modification and the social and ethical problems it raises. Leaning back on an overstuffed couch in his dimly lit office, the professor of psychology and psychiatry at the University of Southern California tells why the inevitability of behavior modification does not scare him.

"There's nothing inherently bad in behavior therapy," he says. "The use of a new technology depends on the way society uses people—and we've always been cruel to people. The new technologies, if anything, may be less painful to the victims, which, of course, doesn't say much. But the thing that makes behavior therapy *not* dangerous is an aware public. It will become better known, more accepted and more widely— and discriminately—used."

London once told the American Association for the Advancement of Science: "You can probably get away with almost any kind of change, no matter how strongly people feel about it, if you do it gradually enough in the first place, and if they have anything at all to gain from it in the second. . . . In the case of behavior control, [this] suggests some very dramatic changes may be forthcoming."

"I don't think there's much danger of this stuff running wild," London says. "So far, agencies of social control are very conservative in using it. And, as I said, ultimately the most important kind of control is public opinion." London says he is "very suspicious" of prison experiments, but "prison is a lunatic situation and you're talking about what is less or more crazy; I'd be inclined to limit most of the coercion in prison. It's really not clear to me what difference there is between forced marching in a yard and most behavior control experiments."

Despite his warm, or at least neutral feelings toward other aspects of behavior modification, London is down on the punishment cure. "I think the techniques of aversion therapy are terrible," he says. "*A Clockwork Orange* was a picnic compared to some of the things that have gone on. It's pretty awful to hurt people when you don't have to, with no clear evidence that you're benefiting them. If anything is clear in the literature it's that aversion therapy isn't worth much. Maybe if someone really wants to give up something, it can be helpful by giving them a feedback signal. If so, then when it does work it's because a person was in need of a mental cue that reminds him what he wants to accomplish.

"The problem of how to select methods of treatment is that the patient—the consumer—to begin with doesn't know what's good for him. So you have to exercise some kind of control over the vendor, but there isn't any easy, legitimate way to do that. I don't think the long-range future of aversion therapy is promising. It's easy to use, and it gets some preliminary results, but in the long run its use must be justified by

There are, of course, many psychologists who disagree with Perry London. They have used aversion therapy for years and have found it to be sufficiently helpful in enough cases to continue its use. There have been many individual cases reported in which patients who had unsuccessfully undergone other treatments were finally helped to cast off their albatross through aversion therapy. The fact that clouds of controversy hang over the treatment shouldn't, in itself, be a deterrent to its future use.

Yet it is also true that there have been some gross abuses

in using the punishment cure in the name of science—in private doctors' offices as well as prisons and mental institutions. Extravagant claims of success have been made without enough solid evidence. Sometimes it seems as though practitioners of aversion therapy have forgotten that it is a quantum jump from research on laboratory animals to treatment of humans. A number of lawsuits have been filed to challenge the use of conditioning behind barred windows, and the initial decisions are in favor of the inmates and against the intrusion of the state into the mental processes of its charges. Both state and federal laws, Congressional hearings and a sharpened awareness by the public seem certain to make it even more difficult in the future to use aversion therapy in institutions without strict guidelines and a legitimate concern for the rights of the inmates.

For voluntary patients, the profession itself must develop clear sets of standards concerning which aversive techniques to use, how to use them, on whom and when. Clients have to be made aware of alternative treatments and any possible risks of the punishment cure. Therapists must go through some sort of certification process to assure that they have the proper level of competence; as it stands now, anyone walking in off the street could practice aversion therapy without knowing anything more than how to turn on the shocker. Research activities need to be better coordinated so that there will be a basis for comparing studies to determine once and for all whether aversive conditioning is a valuable tool to help people change their unwanted behavior—or just a throwback to the dunkings and spinnings that passed for treatment 200 years ago. It is becoming increasingly evident that if behavior therapists don't take some action on their own—and soon— then someone else will, and we all will be the worse for it. Ultimate control of the human mind and behavior must remain with the individual. It is our most sacred possession.

REFERENCES AND ACKNOWLEDGMENTS

CHAPTER I

Bandura, Albert. *Principles of Behavior Modification.* New York: Holt, Rinehart and Winston, 1969. Reprinted by permission of Holt, Rinehart and Winston.

Burgess, Anthony. *A Clockwork Orange.* New York: W. W. Norton, 1963.

Farrall Instrument Company. *Behavior Modification Equipment.* Catalog No. F72. Grand Island, Neb.: Author, 1972.

Gruber, Ronald P. Behavior therapy: Problems in generalization. *Behavior Therapy,* 1971, *2,* 361-368.

Hunter, Richard, and MacAlpine, Ida. *Three Hundred Years of Psychiatry.* London: Oxford University Press, 1963.

Rachman, S., and Teasdale, J. *Aversion Therapy and Behaviour Disorders: An Analysis.* Coral Gables, Fla.: University of Miami Press, 1969.

Rattray, R. S. *Ashanti Law and Constitution.* London: Oxford Clarendon Press, 1929.

Sheehan, J. G. Reflections on the behavioral modification of stuttering. In Ainsworth, S. (Ed.), *Conditioning and Stut-*

185

tering Therapy: Applications and Limitations. Memphis: Speech Foundation of America, 1970.

Skinner, B. F. Beyond Freedom and Dignity. New York: Alfred A. Knopf, 1971.

Tanner, Barry A. Aversive shock issues: Physical danger, emotional harm, effectiveness and "dehumanization." Journal of Behaviour Therapy and Experimental Psychiatry, 1973, 4, 113-115.

CHAPTER II

Alcohol and Alcoholism: Problems, Programs and Progress. Washington, D.C.: U.S. Government Printing Office, 1972.

Blake, B. George. The application of behavior therapy to the treatment of alcoholism. Behaviour Research and Therapy, 1965, 3, 75-85.

Blake, B. George. A follow-up of alcoholics treated by behavior therapy. Behaviour Research and Therapy, 1967, 5, 89-94.

Cautela, Joseph R. Rationale and procedure for covert conditioning. In Richard D. Rubin, et al. (Eds.), Advances in Behavior Therapy. New York: Academic Press, 1972.

Clancy, John; Vanderhoof, E.; and Campbell, P. Evaluation of an aversive technique as a treatment for alcoholism. Quarterly Journal of Studies on Alcohol, 1967, 28, 476-485.

Davidson, Robert S. Aversive modification of alcoholic behavior: I. Punishment of an alcohol-reinforced operant. Unpublished manuscript, 1973.

Davidson, Robert S. Comparative analyses of adversive conditioning in alcoholism. In J. H. Masserman (Ed.), Current Psychiatric Therapies (Vol. 13). New York: Grune & Stratton, 1973 (pp. 141-148).

Davidson, Robert S., and Wallach, Edward S. Shock facilitation and suppression of alcohol- and coke-maintained behavior. Psychological Reports, 1972, 31, 415-424.

Dunn, Robert B. A new comprehensive, intensive care program for the treatment of alcoholism. *Psychosomatics,* 1972, *13,* 397-400.

Farrar, C. H.; Powell, Barbara J.; and Martin, L. K. Punishment of alcohol consumption by apneic paralysis. *Behaviour Research and Therapy,* 1968, *6,* 13-16.

Gordon, William Winton. The treatment of alcohol (and tobacco) addiction by differential conditioning. *American Journal of Psychotherapy,* 1971, *25,* 394-418.

Kantorovich, N. V. An attempt of curing alcoholism by associated reflexes. *Novoye Refleksologii Nervnoy i Fiziologii Sistemy,* 1928, *3,* 436-445.

Lehigh Valley Electronics. *Aversive Electric Shock: A Handbook for the Behavioral Laboratory.* Fogelsville, Pa.: undated.

Lemere, Frederick, and Voegtlin, Walter L. An evaluation of the aversion treatment of alcoholism. *Quarterly Journal of Studies on Alcohol,* 1950, *11,* 199-204.

Madill, Mary-Frances; Campbell, Dugal; Laverty, S. G.; Sanderson, R. E.; and Vandewater, S. L. Aversion treatment of alcoholics by succinylcholine-induced apneic paralysis. *Quarterly Journal of Studies on Alcohol,* 1966, *27,* 483-509.

McCance, C., and McCance, P. F. Alcoholism in North-East Scotland: Its treatment and outcome. *British Journal of Psychiatry,* 1969, *115,* 189-198.

McGuire, R. J., and Vallance, M. Aversion therapy by electric shock: A simple technique. *British Medical Journal,* 1964, *1,* 151-153.

Miller, Peter M., and Hersen, Michel. Quantitative changes in alcohol consumption as a function of electrical aversive conditioning. *Journal of Clinical Psychology,* 1972, *28,* 590-593.

Miller, Peter M.; Hersen, Michel; Eisler, Richard M.; and Hemphill, Diana P. Electrical aversion therapy with alcoholics: An analogue study. *Behaviour Research and Therapy,* 1973, *11,* 491-497.

Mottin, J. L. Drug-induced attenuation of alcohol consumption: A review and evaluation of claimed, potential or current therapies. *Quarterly Journal of Studies on Alcohol*, 1973, *34*, 444-472.

Portnov, A. A., and Pyatnitskaya, I. N. *Klinika Alkogolizma*. Leningrad: Meditsina, 1971. Reviewed by Efron, Vera. *Quarterly Journal of Studies on Alcohol*, 1973, *34*, 664-666.

Rachman, S. Controlled drinking for alcoholism. Letter in *British Medical Journal*, 1972, *2*, 591. Reprinted by permission of the *British Medical Journal*.

Sanderson, R. E.; Campbell, D.; and Laverty, S. G. An investigation of a new aversive conditioning treatment for alcoholism. *Quarterly Journal of Studies on Alcohol*, 1963, *24*, 261-275.

Smith, James W.; Lemere, Frederick; and Dunn, Robert B. Pentothal interviews in the treatment of alcoholism. *Psychosomatics*, 1971, *12*, 330-331.

Sobell, Mark B., and Sobell, Linda C. Individualized behavior therapy for alcoholics. *California Mental Health Research Monograph No. 13*, 1972.

Sobell, Mark B., and Sobell, Linda C. Alcoholics treated by individualized behavior therapy: One year treatment outcome. *Behaviour Research and Therapy*, 1973, *11*, 599-618.

Sobell, Mark B., and Sobell, Linda C. Evidence of controlled drinking by former alcoholics: A second-year evaluation. Paper presented at 81st Annual Convention of American Psychological Association, August 31, 1973.

Stojiljković, S. Conditioned aversion treatment of alcoholics. *Quarterly Journal of Studies on Alcohol*, 1969, *30*, 900-904.

Voegtlin, Walter L., and Broz, William R. The conditioned reflex treatment of chronic alcoholism. X. An analysis of 3125 admissions over a period of ten and a half years. *Annals of Internal Medicine*, 1949, *30*, 580-597.

Wilson, G. Terence. Outcome research strategies in behavior therapy: Issues and evidence from the treatment of alcoholics. Paper presented to American Psychopathological Association, March 7, 1974.

Wilson, G. Terence; Leaf, Russell; and Nathan, Peter E. The aversive control of excessive drinking by chronic alcoholics in the laboratory setting. Unpublished manuscript, 1974.

Wilson, G. Terence, and Rosen, Raymond C. Training controlled drinking in an alcoholic through a multifaceted behavioral treatment program: A case study. Unpublished manuscript, 1974.

CHAPTER III

Cautela, J. R. Treatment of smoking by covert sensitization. Reprinted with permission of author and publisher from: PSYCHOLOGICAL REPORTS, 1970, *26*, 415–420.

Franks, Cyril M.; Fried, Robert; and Ashem, Beatrice. An improved apparatus for the aversive conditioning of cigarette smokers. *Behaviour Research and Therapy*, 1966, *4*, 301-308.

Fredrickson, Donald T. Cigarette smoking: Questions patients ask doctors. *Chest*, 1970, *58*, 147-151; 369-372.

Grimaldi, Karen E., and Lichtenstein, Edward. Hot, smoky air as an aversive stimulus in the treatment of smoking. *Behaviour Research and Therapy*, 1969, *7*, 275-282.

Keutzer, Carolin S. Behavior modification of smoking: The experimental investigation of diverse techniques. *Behaviour Research and Therapy*, 1968, *6*, 137-157.

Lichtenstein, Edward. How to quit smoking. Reprinted from PSYCHOLOGY TODAY Magazine, January 1971. Copyright © 1970 Ziff-Davis Publishing Company. All rights reserved.

Lichtenstein, Edward, and Keutzer, Carolin S. Experimental investigation of diverse techniques to modify smoking: A follow-up report. *Behaviour Research and Therapy*, 1969, *7*, 139-140.

Marrone, Robert L.; Merksamer, Mary Ann; and Salzberg, Philip M. A short duration group treatment of smoking behavior by stimulus saturation. *Behaviour Research and Therapy*, 1970, *8*, 347-352.

National Clearinghouse for Smoking and Health. *Smoker's Self-Testing Kit.* Washington, D.C.: U.S. Government Printing Office, 1974.

Russell, M. A. Hamilton. Effect of electric aversion on cigarette smoking. *British Medical Journal,* 1970, *1,* 82-86.

Schwartz, Jerome L. A critical review and evaluation of smoking control methods. *Public Health Reports,* 1969, *84,* 483-506.

Whitman, Thomas L. Modification of chronic smoking behavior: A comparison of three approaches. *Behaviour Research and Therapy,* 1969, *7,* 257-263.

Whitman, Thomas L. Aversive control of smoking behaviour in a group context. *Behaviour Research and Therapy,* 1972, *10,* 97-104.

Wilde, Gerrit Jan S. Behavior therapy for addicted cigarette smokers: A preliminary investigation. *Behaviour Research and Therapy,* 1964, *2,* 107-109.

CHAPTER IV

Alinder, Gary. Off Dr. Bieber! *Los Angeles Free Press,* Aug. 14, 1970 (supp.)

Bieber, B.; Bieber, I.; Bieber, T.; Dain, H. J.; Dince, P. R.; Drellich, M. G.; Grand, H. G.; Grundlach, R. H.; Kremer, M. W.; and Wilber, C. B. *Homosexuality.* New York: Basic Books, 1963.

Bjornson, Lars. Baker protests shock treatments at Minnesota U. *The Advocate,* Jan. 31, 1973, p. 10.

Chapel, James L. Behavior modification. *Canadian Psychiatric Association Journal,* 1970, *15,* 315-318.

Colson, Charles E. Olfactory aversion therapy for homosexual behavior. *Journal of Behaviour Therapy and Experimental Psychiatry,* 1972, *3,* 185-187.

Curtis, R. H., and Presly, A. S. The extinction of homosexual behavior by covert sensitization. *Behaviour Research and Therapy,* 1972, *10,* 81-83.

Davison, Gerald C., and Wilson, G. Terence. Attitudes of behavior therapists toward homosexuality. *Behavior Therapy*, 1973, *4*, 686-696. Copyright Academic Press Inc.

Fatal emetine poisoning from aversion treatment. *Medico Legal Journal*, 1964, *32*(2), 95.

Feldman, M. P., and MacCulloch, M. J. *Homosexual Behaviour: Therapy and Assessment.* Oxford: Pergamon Press, 1971.

Freund, K. Some problems in the treatment of homosexuality. In H. J. Eysenck (Ed.), *Behaviour Therapy and the Neuroses.* London: Pergamon Press, 1960 (pp. 312-326).

Gold, S., and Neufeld, Inge L. A learning approach to the treatment of homosexuality. *Behaviour Research and Therapy*, 1965, *3*, 201-204.

James, Basil. Case of homosexuality treated by aversion therapy. *British Medical Journal*, 1962, *1*, 768-770.

James, Basil, and Early, Donal F. Aversion therapy for homosexuality. Letter in *British Medical Journal*, 1963, *1*, 538.

Larson, Donald E. An adaptation of the Feldman and MacCulloch approach to treatment of homosexuality by the application of anticipatory avoidance learning. *Behaviour Research and Therapy*, 1970, *8*, 209-210.

Maletzky, Barry M. The treatment of homosexuality by "assisted" covert sensitization. *Behaviour Research and Therapy*, 1973, *11*, 655-657.

Mandel, Karl H. Preliminary report on a new aversion therapy for male homosexuals. *Behaviour Research and Therapy*, 1970, *8*, 93-95.

Max, L. W. Breaking up a homosexual fixation by the conditioned reaction technique: A case study. *Psychological Bulletin*, 1935, *32*, 734.

McConaghy, N. Subjective and penile plethysmograph responses following aversion-relief and apomorphine aversion therapy for homosexual impulses. *British Journal of Psychiatry*, 1969, *115*, 723-730.

McConaghy, N. Aversive therapy of homosexuality: Measures of efficacy. *American Journal of Psychiatry*, 1971, *127*, 141-144.

McConaghy, N., and Barr, R. F. Classical, avoidance and

backward conditioning treatments of homosexuality. *British Journal of Psychiatry*, 1973, *122*, 151-162.

Miller, M. M. Hypnotic-aversion treatment of homosexuality. *Journal of the National Medical Association*, 1963, *55*, 411-415.

Quinn, J. T.; Harbison, J. J. M.; and McAllister, H. An attempt to shape human penile responses. *Behaviour Research and Therapy*, 1970, *8*, 213-216.

Shealy, Allen E. Combining behavior therapy and cognitive therapy in treating homosexuality. *Psychotherapy: Theory, Research and Practice*, 1972, *9*, 221-222.

Shock "cure" study denied hospital okay. *The Advocate*, Dec. 22, 1971, p. 5.

Shock device booth zapped at conference. *The Advocate*, May 9, 1973, p. 9.

Silverstein, Charles. Behavior modification and the gay community. Paper presented to the Association for the Advancement of Behavior Modification, Oct. 8, 1972.

Tanner, Barry A. Shock intensity and fear of shock in the modification of homosexual behavior in males by avoidance learning. *Behaviour Research and Therapy*, 1973, *11*, 213-218.

Wilson, G. Terence, and Davison, Gerald C. Behavior therapy and homosexuality: A critical perspective. *Behavior Therapy*, 1974, *5*, 16-28.

CHAPTER V

Abel, Gene G.; Levis, Donald J.; and Clancy, John. Aversion therapy applied to taped sequences of deviant behavior in exhibitionism and other sexual deviations: A preliminary report. *Journal of Behaviour Therapy and Experimental Psychiatry*, 1970, *1*, 59-66.

Annon, Jack S. The therapeutic use of masturbation in the treatment of sexual disorders. In Richard D. Rubin, et al. (Eds.), *Advances in Behavior Therapy* (Vol. 4). New York: Academic Press, 1973.

Barlow, David H.; Reynolds, E. Joyce; and Agras, W. Stewart. Gender identity change in a transsexual. *Archives of General Psychiatry,* 1973, *28,* 569-576.

Blakemore, C. B.; Thorpe, J. G.; Barker, J. C.; Conway, C. G.; and Lavin, N. I. The application of faradic aversion conditioning in a case of transvestism. *Behaviour Research and Therapy,* 1963, *1,* 29-34.

Blakemore, C. B.; Thorpe, J. G.; Barker, J. C.; Conway, C. G.; and Lavin, N. I. Follow-up note to: The application of faradic aversion conditioning in a case of transvestism. *Behaviour Research and Therapy,* 1963, *1,* 191.

Bond, I. K., and Evans, D. R. Avoidance therapy: Its use in two cases of underwear fetishism. *Canadian Medical Association Journal,* 1967, *96,* 1160-1162.

Breckon, William. How electric shocks took Mr. X's mind off his mistress. (London) *Daily Mail,* Dec. 3, 1966.

Davison, Gerald C. Elimination of a sadistic fantasy by a client-controlled counter conditioning technique. *Journal of Abnormal Psychology,* 1968, *73,* 84-90.

Denholtz, Myron. The use of tape recordings between therapy sessions. *Journal of Behaviour Therapy and Experimental Psychiatry,* 1970, *1,* 139-143.

Evans, D. R. Masturbatory fantasy and sexual deviation. *Behaviour Research and Therapy,* 1968, *6,* 17-19.

Evans, D. R. Subjective variables and treatment effects in aversion therapy. *Behaviour Research and Therapy,* 1970, *8,* 147-152.

Fookes, B. H. Some experiences in the use of aversion therapy in male homosexuality, exhibitionism and fetishism-transvestism. *British Journal of Psychiatry,* 1969, *115,* 339-341.

Kohlenberg, Robert J. Treatment of a homosexual pedophiliac using in vivo desensitization: A case study. *Journal of Abnormal Psychology,* 1974, *83,* 192-195.

Lavin, N. I.; Thorpe, J. G.; Barker, J. C.; Blakemore, C. B.; and Conway, C. G. Behavior therapy in a case of transvestism. *Journal of Nervous and Mental Diseases,* 1961, *133,* 346-353.

Marks, Isaac; Gelder, Michael; and Bancroft, John. Sexual deviants two years after electrical aversion. *British Journal of Psychiatry*, 1970, *117*, 173-185.

Marks, I. M.; Rachman, S.; and Gelder, M. G. Methods for assessment of aversion treatment in fetishism with masochism. *Behaviour Research and Therapy*, 1965, *3*, 253-258.

Marquis, John N. Orgasmic reconditioning: Changing sexual object choice through controlling masturbation fantasies. *Journal of Behaviour Therapy and Experimental Psychiatry*, 1970, *1*, 263-271.

McGuire, R. J.; Carlisle, J. M.; and Young, B. G. Sexual deviation as conditioned behavior: A hypothesis. *Behaviour Research and Therapy*, 1965, *2*, 185-190.

Oswald, Ian. Introduction of illusory and hallucinatory voices with considerations of behavior therapy. *Journal of Mental Science*, 1962, *108*, 196-212.

Rachman, S. Sexual fetishism: An experimental analogue. *Psychological Record*, 1966, *16*, 293-296.

Raymond, M. J. Case of fetishism treated by aversion therapy. *British Medical Journal*, 1956, *2*, 854-857.

Raymond, Michael, and O'Keeffe, Kevin. A case of pin-up fetishism treated by aversion conditioning. *British Journal of Psychiatry*, 1965, *111*, 579-581.

Serber, Michael. Shame aversion therapy. *Journal of Behaviour Therapy and Experimental Psychiatry*, 1970, *1*, 213-215.

Serber, Michael. Shame aversion therapy with and without heterosexual retraining. In Richard D. Rubin, et al. (Eds.), *Advances in Behavior Therapy*. New York: Academic Press, 1972.

Strupp, Hans H. Some observations on the fallacy of value-free psychotherapy and the empty organism. *Journal of Abnormal Psychology*, 1974, *83*, 199-201.

Thorpe, J. G.; Schmidt, E.; Brown, P. T.; and Castell, D. Aversion-relief therapy: A new method for general application. *Behaviour Research and Therapy*, 1964, *2*, 71-82.

Wickramasekera, Ian. A technique for controlling a certain type of sexual exhibitionism. *Psychotherapy: Theory, Research and Practice*, 1972, *9*, 207-210.

CHAPTER VI

Adams, Kenneth M.; Klinge, Valerie; and Keiser, Thomas W. The extinction of a self-injurious behavior in an epileptic child. *Behaviour Research and Therapy,* 1973, *11,* 351-356.

Antman, Elliott M. Flooding in vivo for a case of vermiphobia. *Journal of Behaviour Therapy and Experimental Psychiatry,* 1973, *4,* 275-277.

Bass, Barry A. An unusual behavioral technique for treating obsessive ruminations. *Psychotherapy: Theory, Research and Practice,* 1973, *10,* 191-192.

Browning, Robert M. Treatment effects of a total behavior modification program with five autistic children. *Behaviour Research and Therapy,* 1971, *9,* 319-327.

Bucher, Bradley, and Lovaas, O. Ivar. Use of aversive stimulation in behavior modification. In Marshall R. Jones (Ed.), *Miami Symposium on the Prediction of Behavior, 1967: Aversive Stimulation.* Coral Gables, Fla.: University of Miami Press, 1968 (pp. 77-145).

Conway, John B., and Bucher, Bradley D. "Soap in the mouth" as an aversive consequence. *Behavior Therapy,* 1974, *5,* 154-156.

Crowe, Michael J.; Marks, Isaac M.; Agras, W. Stewart; and Leitenberg, Harold. Time-limited desensitization, implosion and shaping for phobic patients: A crossover study. *Behaviour Research and Therapy,* 1972, *10,* 319-328.

Denholtz, Myron S. "At home" aversion treatment of compulsive fire-setting behavior: Case report. In Richard D. Rubin, et al. (Eds.), *Advances in Behavior Therapy.* New York: Academic Press, 1972 (pp. 81-84).

Greene, Robert J., and Hoats, David L. Aversive tickling: A simple conditioning technique. *Behavior Therapy,* 1971, *2,* 389-393.

Hogan, Robert A. Implosively oriented behavior modification: Therapy considerations. *Behaviour Research and Therapy,* 1969, *7,* 177-183.

Kenny, F. T.; Solyom, L.; and Solyom, C. Faradic disruption of obsessive ideation in the treatment of obsessive neurosis. *Behavior Therapy,* 1973, *4,* 448-457.

Libet, Julian; Sajwaj, Thomas; and Agras, W. Stewart. Elimination of persistent vomiting in an infant by response-contingent punishment using lemon juice. *Proceedings, 81st Annual Convention, American Psychological Association,* 1973, 921-922.

Lovaas, O. Ivar; Schaeffer, Benson; and Simmons, James Q. Building social behavior in autistic children by use of electric shock. *Journal of Experimental Research in Personality,* 1965, *1,* 99-109.

Lovaas, O. Ivar; Schreibman, Laura; and Koegel, Robert L. A behavior modification approach to the treatment of autistic children. Paper to appear in E. Shopler and R. Reichler (Eds.), *Proceedings of the First International Leo Kanner Colloquium on Child Development, Deviations and Treatment.*

Lovaas, O. Ivar, and Simmons, James Q. Manipulation of self-destruction in three retarded children. *Journal of Applied Behavior Analysis,* 1969, *2,* 143-157.

MacPherson, Evan L. R. Selective operant conditioning and deconditioning of assertive modes of behavior. *Journal of Behaviour Therapy and Experimental Psychiatry,* 1972, *3,* 99-102.

Merbaum, Michael. The modification of self-destructive behavior by a mother-therapist using aversive stimulation. *Behavior Therapy,* 1973, *4,* 442-447.

Sage, Wayne. Autism's Child. *Human Behavior,* 1974, *3,* 16-26.

Scholander, Torkel. Treatment of an unusual case of compulsive behavior by aversive stimulation. *Behavior Therapy,* 1972, *3,* 290-293.

Solyom, L.; Heseltine, G. F. D.; McClure, D. J.; Ledwidge, B.; and Kenny, F. A comparative study of aversion relief and systematic desensitization in the treatment of phobias. *British Journal of Psychiatry,* 1971, *119,* 299-303.

Solyom, L. and Kingstone, E. An obsessive neurosis following morning glory seed ingestion treated by aversion relief. *Journal of Behaviour Therapy and Experimental Psychiatry,* 1973, *4,* 293-295.

Solyom, L.; Shugar, Richard; Bryntwick, Shirley; and Solyom, Carol. Treatment of fear of flying. *American Journal of Psychiatry*, 1973, *130*, 423-427.

Solyom, L., and Miller, S. B. Reciprocal inhibition by aversion relief in the treatment of phobias. *Behaviour Research and Therapy*, 1967, *5*, 313-324.

Stampfl, Thomas G., and Levis, Donald J. Implosive therapy —a behavioral therapy? *Behaviour Research and Therapy*, 1968, *6*, 31-36.

Tate, B. G., and Baroff, George S. Aversive control of self-injurious behavior in a psychotic boy. *Behaviour Research and Therapy*, 1966, *4*, 281-287.

Wisocki, Patricia A. Treatment of obsessive-compulsive behavior by covert sensitization and covert reinforcement: A case report. *Journal of Behaviour Therapy and Experimental Psychiatry*, 1970, *1*, 233-239.

Wolpe, Joseph. For phobia: A hair of the hound. *Psychology Today*, 1969, *3*, 34-37.

CHAPTER VII

Alexander, A. Barney; Chai, Hyman; Creer, Thomas L.; Miklich, Donald R.; Renne, Charles M.; and Cardoso, R. Ronald de A. The elimination of chronic cough by response suppression shaping. *Journal of Behaviour Therapy and Experimental Psychiatry*, 1973, *4*, 75-80.

Ashem, Beatrice; Poser, Ernest; and Trudell, Paul. The use of covert sensitization in the treatment of overeating. In Richard D. Rubin, et al. (Eds.), *Advances in Behavior Therapy*. New York: Academic Press, 1972 (pp. 97-103).

Atthowe, John M., Jr. Controlling nocturnal enuresis in severely disabled and chronic patients. *Behavior Therapy*, 1972, *3*, 232-239.

Barnard, George W.; Flesher, Carol K.; and Steinbook, Richard M. The treatment of urinary retention by aversive stimulus cessation and assertive training. *Behaviour Research and Therapy*, 1966, *4*, 232-236.

Bucher, Bradley D. A pocket-portable shock device with application to nailbiting. *Behaviour Research and Therapy,* 1968, *6,* 389-392.

Cotler, Sherwin B. The use of different behavioral techniques in treating a case of compulsive gambling. *Behavior Therapy,* 1971, *2,* 579-584.

Crosby, N. D. Essential enuresis: Successful treatment based on physiological concepts. *Medical Journal of Australia,* 1950, *23,* 533-542.

Droppa, David C. Behavioral treatment of drug addiction: A review and analysis. *The International Journal of the Addictions,* 1973, *8,* 143-161.

Farrall Instrument Company. Stop needle ritual. Sheet from *Farrall Instrument Company Catalog,* Grand Island, Neb.: Author, undated.

Foreyt, John Paul, and Kennedy, Wallace A. Treatment of overweight by aversion therapy. *Behaviour Research and Therapy,* 1971, *9,* 29-34.

Forsythe, W. I., and Redmond, A. Enuresis and the electric alarm: Study of 200 cases. *British Medical Journal,* 1970, *1,* 211-213.

Goorney, A. B. Treatment of a compulsive horse race gambler by aversion therapy. *British Journal of Psychiatry,* 1968, *114,* 329-333.

Heller, Robert F., and Strang, Harold R. Controlling bruxism through automated aversive conditioning. *Behaviour Research and Therapy,* 1973, *11,* 327-329.

Janda, Louis H., and Rimm, David C. Covert sensitization in the treatment of obesity. *Journal of Abnormal Psychology,* 1972, *80,* 37-42.

Koller, K. M. Treatment of poker-machine addicts by aversion therapy. *Medical Journal of Australia,* 1972, *1,* 742-745.

Lesser, Edward. Behavior therapy with a narcotics user: A case report. *Behaviour Research and Therapy,* 1967, *5,* 251-252.

Liberman, Robert. Aversive conditioning of drug addicts: A pilot study. *Behaviour Research and Therapy,* 1968, *6,* 229-231.

Lovibond, S. H. *Conditioning and Enuresis.* Oxford: Pergamon Press, 1964.

Millard, D. W. A conditioning treatment for "giggle micturation." *Behaviour Research and Therapy,* 1966, *4,* 229-231.

Morganstern, Kenneth P. Cigarette smoke as a noxious stimulus in self-managed aversion therapy for compulsive eating: Technique and case illustration. *Behavior Therapy,* 1974, *5,* 255-260.

Mowrer, O. H., and Mowrer, Willie Mae. Enuresis: A method for its study and treatment. *American Journal of Orthopsychiatry,* 1938, *8,* 436-459.

O'Brien, J. S.; Raynes, A. E.; and Patch, V. D. Treatment of heroin addiction with aversion therapy, relaxation training and systematic desensitization. *Behaviour Research and Therapy,* 1972, *10,* 77-80.

Ratliff, Richard G., and Stein, Norman H. Treatment of neurodermatitis by behavior therapy: A case study. *Behaviour Research and Therapy,* 1968, *6,* 397-399.

Raymond, M. J. The treatment of addiction by aversion conditioning with apomorphine. *Behaviour Research and Therapy,* 1964, *1,* 287-291.

Seager, C. Philip. Learning not to bet. *Mental Health (London),* 1969, Winter, 19-21.

Seager, C. P. Treatment of compulsive gamblers by electrical aversion. *British Journal of Psychiatry,* 1970, *117,* 545-553.

Stunkard, A. J. The management of obesity. *New York State Journal of Medicine,* 1958, *58,* 79-87.

Tough, J. H.; Hawkins, Robert P.; McArthur, M. Moira; and Van Ravensway, Sue. Modification of enuretic behavior by punishment: A new use for an old device. *Behavior Therapy,* 1971, *2,* 567-574.

Ubell, Earl. *How to Save Your Life.* New York: Harcourt Brace Jovanovich, 1973.

Watkins, John T. Treatment of chronic vomiting and extreme emaciation by an aversive stimulus: Case study. *Psychological Reports,* 1972, *31,* 803-805.

Wijesinghe, B. Massed electrical aversion treatment of compulsive eating. *Journal of Behaviour Therapy and Experimental Psychiatry*, 1973, *4*, 133-135.

Wisocki, Patricia A. The successful treatment of a heroin addict by covert conditioning techniques. *Journal of Behaviour Therapy and Experimental Psychiatry*, 1973, *4*, 55-61.

Wolpe, Joseph. Conditioned inhibition of craving in drug addiction: A pilot experiment. *Behaviour Research and Therapy*, 1965, *2*, 285-288.

Young, G. C., and Morgan, R. T. T. Overlearning in the conditioning treatment of enuresis: A long-term follow-up study. *Behaviour Research and Therapy*, 1972, *10*, 419-420.

CHAPTER VIII

Adverse effects of aversive conditioning in institutional settings. Transcript of panel discussion at Camarillo State Hospital, Oct. 11, 1968.

Bauer, Diane. Judge terms Patuxent "most odorous rat hole." *Washington Daily News*, June 30, 1972.

Brandsma, Jeffrey M., and Stein, Leonard I. The use of punishment as a treatment modality: A case report. *Journal of Nervous and Mental Disease*, 1973, *156*, 30-37.

Cole, Rob. Atascadero reformer denies aversion used. *The Advocate*, May 10, 1972, p. 16.

Cole, Rob. Aversion therapy: How bad is real? *The Advocate*, Sept. 27, 1972, pp. 12-13.

Cotter, Lloyd H. Operant conditioning in a Vietnamese mental hospital. *American Journal of Psychiatry*, 1967, *124*, 23-28. Copyright 1967, the American Psychiatric Association.

Crowder, James E., and Harbin, Roger. The effect of punishment on stuttering: A case study. *Psychotherapy: Theory, Research and Practice*, 1971, *8*, 179-180.

Crowley, Brian. Maryland's defective delinquent law nightmarish prelude to 1984. Paper delivered to Medical Correctional Association, Oct. 23, 1971.

Di Spoldo, Nick. Arizona's "Clockwork Orange" bill. *New York Times,* June 20, 1974.

Driscoll, James G. A parent's greatest fear. *National Observer,* March 16, 1974, p. 1.

Kellan, Alexander M. P. Shop lifting treated by aversion to a film. *Behaviour Research and Therapy,* 1969, *7,* 125-127.

Knecht v. Gillman. Opinion of U.S. Court of Appeals for the Eighth Circuit, No. 73-1374, Dec. 5, 1973.

Knight, Michael. Child molesters try shock cure. *New York Times,* May 21, 1974, p. 43.

Livingston, Gary. *Exile's End.* London: Lyrebird Press, 1973 (pp. 101-102).

Ludwig, Arnold M.; Max, Arnold J.; Hill, Philip A.; and Browning, Robert M. The control of violent behavior through faradic shock. *The Journal of Nervous and Mental Disease,* 1969, *148,* 624-637.

Mattocks, Arthur L., and Jew, Charles. Assessment of an aversive treatment program with extreme acting-out patients in a psychiatric facility for criminal offenders. Unpublished study.

McConnell, James V. Criminals can be brain washed—now. *Psychology Today,* April, 1970, *3.*

Reimringer, Martin J.; Morgan, Sterling W.; and Bramwell, Paul F. Succinylcholine as a modifier of acting-out behavior. *Clinical Medicine,* 1970, *77,* 28-29.

Rubin, R. D.; Friend, R.; and Franks, C. M. New application of ECT. In R. D. Rubin and C. M. Franks, *Advances in Behavior Therapy.* New York: Academic Press, 1969.

Scaring the Devil out. *Medical World News,* Oct. 9, 1970, 29-30.

Serber, Michael, and Keith, Claudia G. Offering meaningful services to the institutionalized homosexual: Another deprived minority group. *The Advocate,* June 20, 1973, pp. 2; 18-19.

Spece, Roy G., Jr. Conditioning and other technologies used to "treat?" "rehabilitate?" "demolish?" prisoners and mental patients. *Southern California Law Review,* Spring 1972, *45,* 615-684.

Stanford, Phil. A model, clockwork-orange prison. *New York Times Magazine,* Sept. 17, 1972, p. 9.
THIS CHILD IS RATED X. Transcript of NBC News "White Paper on Juvenile Justice" aired May 2, 1971. Produced and written by Martin Carr for NBC News. © Copyright 1971 National Broadcasting Company, Inc. Reprinted by permission.

CHAPTER IX

Delgado, José M. R. *Physical Control of the Mind.* New York: Harper & Row, 1969.
Halleck, Seymour L. Legal and ethical aspects of behavior control. *American Journal of Psychiatry,* 1974, *131,* 381-385. Copyright 1974, the American Psychiatric Association.
Heath, Robert G. Pleasure and brain activity in man. *The Journal of Nervous and Mental Diseases,* 1972, *154,* 3-18.
Ingraham, Barton L., and Smith, Gerald W. The use of electronics in the observation and control of human behavior and its possible use in rehabilitation and parole. *Issues in Criminology,* 1972, *7,* 35-53.
London, Perry. *Behavior Control.* New York: Harper & Row, 1971.
London, Perry. Social Issues of Behavior Control: Present and Prospective. Paper presented to American Association for the Advancement of Science, Dec. 27, 1972.
Schaefer, Halmuth H. The ethics of deprivation. In *Advances in Behavior Therapy—1968.* New York: Academic Press, 1969, (pp. 83-92). Copyright Academic Press Inc.
Schwitzgebel, Ralph K. Electronic alternatives to imprisonment. *Lex et Scientia,* 1968, *5,* 99-104.
Schwitzgebel, Ralph. Development of an electronic rehabilitation system for parolees. *Law and Computer Technology,* 1969, *2,* 9-12.
Schwitzgebel, Ralph K. *Development and Legal Regulation of Coercive Behavior Modification Techniques with Of-*

fenders. Washington, D.C.: U.S. Government Printing Office, 1971.

Schwitzgebel, Ralph; Schwitzgebel, Robert; Pahnke, Walter N.; and Hurd, William S. A program of research in behavioral electronics. *Behavioral Science,* 1964, *9,* 233-238.

Schwitzgebel, Robert L. Survey of electromechanical devices for behavior modification. *Psychological Bulletin,* 1968, *70,* 444-459.

Schwitzgebel, Robert L. A belt from big brother. *Psychology Today,* 1969, *2,* 45-47; 65.

Shapiro, Michael H. The uses of behavior control technologies: A response. *Issues in Criminology,* 1972, *7,* 55-93.

INDEX

205